BEYOND *the* UNDERGROUND

—

Aunt Harriet,
MOSES OF HER PEOPLE

JOYCE STOKES JONES
MICHELE JONES GALVIN

Sankofa Media
Syracuse, New York

Sankofa Media books may be ordered through booksellers or by contacting:

Sankofa Media
409 Crawford Avenue
Syracuse, New York 13224

sankofamediaone@gmail.com
www.mosesofherpeople.com

Editor Courtney Rae Kasper
Cover Illustration London Ladd
Cover Design Karen Nelson

Chapter Five initially published in aaduna, Volume 2, No. 2

ISBN: 978-0-9895755-1-5

Library of Congress Control Number: 2013913987

Printed in the United States of America

DEDICATION

—

For my children, their children, their children's children, and all members of the Harriet Ross Tubman Davis family.

To Alex and Jom Graves

Warm wishes and enjoy!

Best

Jayne Straker Joxes

CONTENTS

—

ACKNOWLEDGMENTS

—

The researching and writing of this book was a labor of love that spanned three decades. Its completion is not a singular achievement, but one that was gained by the involvement of many people. We the authors extend our deep appreciation to everyone who has shown us love, support, and encouragement throughout the journey of writing and publishing Beyond the Underground: Aunt Harriet, Moses of Her People. We want to give our special thanks to the following people:

First and foremost, we give thanks to God for this journey, which allowed us to uncover and write about our family ties to Modesty, Rittia, Sophe, Ann Marie, and to one of the greatest American heroines, Harriet Ross Tubman Davis;

Laura Ponticello, our literary agent, who has been the anchor of the strategic planning and whose vision has driven the process of bringing our story into the world;

Kathryn Ruscitto, president of St. Joseph's Hospital, whose leadership and friendship afforded us the opportunity of a lifetime. Through the Heritage Project, her friends and members of the community donated monies for us to travel to Ghana, West Africa, in search of our roots and information to create a more realistic story about our familial heritage;

Nancy Bottar, Peggy Ogden, Vicki Brackens, Anne Messenger, and Kathy Goldfarb-Findling for giving generously of their time and talent to the Heritage Project;

Mark Wright for his time and willingness to provide administrative support to the Heritage Project;

Sheila Tucker, former Cayuga County historian, who assisted in the gathering of archival documents, directories, and articles specific to our family history in Cayuga County;

Adrianne Jones Roderick, genealogical advisor, who spent countless hours delving further into our family history to uncover interesting tidbits that may have otherwise remained unknown, and her husband, Steven Roderick, for his support;

Courtney Rae Kasper, editor, for her invaluable assistance in formatting the book for publication and whose editing expertise has brought to the work outstanding readability;

William E. Berry, Jr. for his constant encouragement, support, and counsel. He was the original editor of Chapter Five: Home Going and published the chapter in the online publication *aaduna;*

London Ladd, artist and illustrator, who created our book's phenomenal cover image;

Karen Nelson, graphic artist and designer, who designed an exceptional cover image for both hardcover and soft cover publications;

Ashtian Holmes, website designer, for his incredible work that brought the book to life before its publication;

Kim Miner for her creativity with the family tree in portraying our maternal lineage to Harriet Tubman Davis;

Sally Roesch Wagner for her friendship and for letting the world know that there is a way to tell the story of Harriet Tubman Davis within the context of her family lineage;

The staff of the Seymour Library in Auburn, New York, for their assistance in researching and compiling information on our family history in Cayuga County;

The staff of the Onondaga Public Library at the Galleries for their patience and willingness to assist us with use of the reference materials;

Arden Phair, former curator of the St. Catharines Museum, Ontario, Canada, for his assistance in accessing archival information and reference materials about family members and Harriet Tubman's life in Canada;

Dr. Kay McElvy for her tremendous body of knowledge on Harriet Tubman and the Underground Railroad, and for her willingness to share it.

Robert Stewart, a descendant of John Trevillion Stewart, who was one of the Ross family's masters. His personal information and assistance were invaluable;

Selene Weiss, a descendant of Dr. Anthony C. Thompson. Thompson was a former master of the Ross family. Weiss' personal information was invaluable;

Herbert Williams, former director of the Community Folk Art Gallery, assisted in locating Robert Stewart and Selene Weiss, who are descendants of former slave masters who owned the Ross family;

Tim Fox, producer at Channel 9 WSYR, who assisted with the production of *A Conversation with a Living Relative of Harriet Tubman*;

Tony Gaskins, news reporter, who was the interviewer and assisted with the production of *A Conversation with a Living Relative of Harriet Tubman*;

Milton "Buzzy" Richardson for recounting many stories and remembrances of incidents and family members who lived on Chapman Avenue during the early twentieth century;

Kwame Otieku, Doris Danchi, and Emmanuel Awuah for their personal connections and assistance with the itinerary and accommodations made for our "Proud Heritage Journey to Ghana";

Joseph Nyarko and his family and Emmanuel Tetteh for attending to our every need while in Ghana;

Alice Norris for providing vivid recollections, photos, and documents about the Norris family who resided in the Harriet

Tubman house after Harriet's death;

Craig Williams, historian at the New York State Museum, for helping to locate the actual gravesite of Thomas Elliott;

Carol Hayes Collier for her personal story and perspective on the history of mental health institutions and issues;

Rickey Bartlett, superintendent of the Willard Treatment Center, and Peggy Ellsworth, of the Romulus Historical Society, who assisted in our efforts to conduct a memorial service at the gravesite of Thomas Elliott at the Willard Asylum Cemetery;

Sehl Burns, Finger Lakes Funeral Association, Herson Funeral Home, and Ithaca Monument for donating the tombstone for Thomas Elliott;

Arethea Brown, Lori Covington, and Vivian Holmes for great memories and photography of our journey to the motherland;

Doris Jackson and Lee Van Allen for their annual welcome and accommodations at Shearer Cottage on Martha's Vineyard. There, the words "The End" were memorably written while sitting on the veranda;

Marc and Carol Jones for their unwavering support and generosity of giving their time and provided counsel on the business side of self-publishing;

Ernestine and Donald Wyatt, Josephine Cross, and Joyce and Kenneth Stewart for their continued support;

Our deepest appreciation to, my husband, John Galvin, and our son, John Galvin, Jr., for their enduring love, support, encouragement, and patience over the years. Words cannot express how much we valued their recommendations and technical assistance.

— Michele Jones Galvin and Joyce Stokes Jones

FOREWORD

—

Say the name Harriet Tubman to any student in the United States from fourth grade on, and they will tell you about the exploits of an iconic conductor who guided more than three hundred enslaved women, children, and men to freedom through the network of safe homes known as the Underground Railroad. "Moses," they will proudly tell you, "never lost a passenger."

Born into slavery and beaten by her Maryland masters, Tubman suffered headaches, seizures, and sudden sleeping spells for most of her life. One of Tubman's former slave owners threw a heavy iron object at her head when she was caught trying to help an enslaved man escape.

Tubman was the first woman to lead an armed expedition during the Civil War, and her raid liberated more than seven hundred enslaved people in South Carolina. Her war service ranged from the following: cook, nurse, armed scout, and spy.

The story of Harriet Tubman—her enslaved early life, freedom fighting, Civil War service and post-war activism, and philanthropic life's work—has been celebrated in numerous forms for all ages, including picture coloring books, elementary school curriculum, popular trade books, and scholarly biographies. Tubman's life has been examined and extolled; what could possibly be new to tell? The story of Harriet Tubman told from the intimate perspective of a family member.

While Tubman had one "adopted" daughter, she also had a number of nieces and nephews who lived close to (and often in) the post-war Harriet Tubman home in Auburn, New York.

They heard the stories first-hand, and they learned the cadence of the voice that shared those stories. The family members continued to keep the intimate memory alive by passing these stories on from generation to generation. And one living relative decided to share the inherited family lore with the rest of the world.

The result is this book. A book written by Harriet Tubman's great-great-grandniece Joyce Stokes Jones, with the assistance of Jones' daughter Michele Jones Galvin, that places the well-known pieces of Tubman's fascinating life in Jones' personal context, while revealing dramatic new information about the family. Transported into the heart of the slave institution, we the readers experience, from an insider's perspective, its devastating effects. Jones takes us with her as she follows Tubman's path from Maryland to the freedom of Canada, and then on a "proud heritage journey" to Ghana in search of Tubman's grandmother Modesty.

This fresh vision of a woman we thought we knew gives us a much deeper appreciation for this American legend.

It is said that when an elder passes another library burns to the ground. We are indeed fortunate that the family legacy of Harriet Tubman has been preserved. With this book, Joyce Stokes Jones has given us her library.

— Sally Roesch Wagner, Executive Director, The Matilda Joslyn Gage Foundation, Fayetteville, New York

PREFACE

—

It is with great pleasure that I present *Beyond the Underground: Aunt Harriet, Moses of Her People*. This creative nonfiction work delves into my family's genealogical roots and its struggle against slavery and racism. But the unique twist is that the story of Harriet Tubman's lineage is told by a great-great-grandniece.

Beyond the Underground chronicles my investigation into the significant events that defined the Green Ross family, while focusing on Harriet (Ross) Tubman—one of America's greatest and bravest heroines. It is a poignant tale that realistically details slavery on the Eastern Shore of Maryland and alludes to the paradox of winning freedom above the Mason-Dixon Line and in Canada. This work's backbone explores the relationships between family members, their slave masters, and friends, all of whom shaped Harriet Tubman's saga.

During the past three decades, I have traveled as far south to an area known historically as Bucktown, Maryland, and as far north as St. Catharines, Ontario, Canada, to unlock my family history. I was fortunate to discover Aunt Harriet's grandmother Modesty and how she courageously survived the Middle Passage as a captured slave from Ghana, West Africa. I became knowledgeable about four of our family's slave masters. I uncovered the abolitionist activities of Aunt Harriet's father and of her mother's belligerence. I learned the horrendous details behind John Tubman's murder (Aunt Harriet's first husband) and of Harriet's second marriage to Nelson Charles Davis, a Civil War veteran. I was awed by Harriet's courage to free her family and other Negroes from Southern bondage—

most importantly being my great-grandmother Ann Marie (Ross) Stewart Elliott. I now know that Aunt Harriet's life was more dynamic and humbling than it is often documented.

As a young girl, I learned that I was related to Harriet Tubman. It was an astounding revelation. I was pleasantly surprised, proud, and mystified all at once. It was an extraordinary and curious thing. Later, I wanted to know more. I wanted to know how my great-grandmother was related to Harriet—was my great-grandmother her sister or a niece? I was bound and determined to found out. I would leave no stone unturned that would reveal my familial relationship to the Moses of Her People. I realized that I had to document what I uncovered... **and a wonderful family story unfolded.** I wanted to leave my children, their children, their children's children, and other relatives a collection of my research and findings. As I continued my work, I thought that there might be others who would also be fascinated by what I had discovered.

While I count penning *Beyond the Underground* to be my greatest achievement, I have celebrated my African American heritage through several other efforts. In the early 1970s, I wrote a recurring column called "Black Heritage" for a local Syracuse newspaper. I also produced a *Black on Black* series for the local public broadcasting network and later on, a video titled *A Conversation with A Living Relative of Harriet Tubman*, followed by a limited edition collection of handmade Harriet Tubman dolls. Today, we have a photographic documentary available that chronicles my Proud Heritage Journey to Ghana.

During the last several years, I have diligently compiled my research and findings into a four-part book. Part One covers my remembrances, experiences, and family memories of their relationship with Harriet Tubman. Part Two more intimately explores the kinship ties of my great-grandparents with the

Moses of Her People. The next part describes the journey of Aunt Harriet's grandmother Modesty across the Middle Passage and concludes with Harriet's escape from the jaws of slavery. The last part deals with Aunt Harriet's life as a free woman in Pennsylvania, New York, and Canada, to the years preceding her death in the small Central New York town of Auburn. Throughout the work I reflect on the contrasts—with regard to race and discrimination—between Aunt Harriet's life and my own.

It is with deep gratitude that I thank my eldest daughter, Michele, whose time, talent, and resources made completing this laborious love possible. I am fully grateful for the love and support from my loving husband, Harry, and daughter Olivia, both of whom are now deceased. My heartfelt thanks also goes out to my other children, Adrianne and Marc, for their steady encouragement and support.

In celebration of Aunt Harriet, I can only hope that sharing my version of her life's story will pay a lasting tribute to her memory and accomplishments. I anticipate that this story will inform you, inspire you, and give you pause for reflection, as you take this literary journey with me into the life and times of Harriet Tubman and her fight for freedom. As a relative of this great heroine, I urge you all to do what is in your power to ensure that freedom is valued and sustained for all people here and across the world.

— Joyce Stokes Jones, great-great-grandniece of Harriet Tubman, the Moses of Her People

THE SYMBOLISM
of the
SANKOFA BIRD

—

The Sankofa Bird is an Adinkra symbol that characterizes the journey we have traveled to create this book. The West African word *sankofa* loosely translated means, "go back and fetch it" or "learn from the past." This symbol speaks to the essence of our work to create a tapestry of the lives of family members that came before us, most notably Harriet Ross Tubman Davis. The image of the Sankofa Bird also reminds us that there is strength in knowing where you came from and upon whose shoulders you stand as free people.

In our family story, we know our freedom was gifted to us by the faith and courage of an American heroine. Harriet Ross Tubman Davis fearlessly sought freedom for her family, for herself, and for her neighbor. There is no greater virtue than being of service to others. The Moses of Her People not only secured the freedom of her family, but she fought for it in the Civil War.

Today, we can all look back at our historical past and appreciate the role she played in liberating our country from the shackles of human bondage. For her descendants, the Sankofa Bird further symbolizes that her legacy lives on.

Part One

—

FAMILY

CHAPTER ONE

—

Reunion

In the summer of 2008, I received an invitation to celebrate my sixtieth high school reunion. This was one of many requests I had received over the years to commemorate the great Class of 1948. I was never overly excited to travel to my hometown of Auburn, New York, to schmooze with former classmates. I always convinced myself that I was too busy or had more important things to do than to mingle about some rented hall pretending that I had a memorable senior year. When I mentioned the latest invite to my daughter Michele, she enthusiastically encouraged me to attend. "It was not every day that someone could say that they attended their sixtieth high school reunion," she reminded me. I guess she had a pretty good point, and since I really had nothing better to do, I took her up on her offer to drive me. Truth be told, I was apprehensive about seeing people from West High who I didn't really know that well. Lord knows that I had not kept in touch with any of them. What was I getting myself into (especially after all that took place that year with the senior play *Girl Shy*)?

Mary Magrino Greene and Madeline Pilla were the organizers behind the reunion. They meticulously identified possible attendees' last known addresses and notified them of the upcoming event. The 1948 graduates of Central, East, Holy Family, and West High Schools were the honored guests. The packet of information indicated that the festivities would kick off with a barbecue dinner on Saturday night. The usual picnic fare was the order of the day: barbecue pork and chicken, hamburgers, hotdogs, salt potatoes, baked beans, baked ziti, and macaroni salad. The weekend-long activities concluded with a Sunday brunch in the Lakeview Country Club ballroom (formerly the Auburn Country Club) on East Lake Road. I had never been to the Lakeview Country Club, or any country club for that matter, so I decided to attend that portion.

After attending nine o'clock morning Mass, Michele and her husband, John, picked me up at my home in Syracuse, New York, on what was an absolutely gorgeous August day. The sky was a robin's-egg blue, the sun was shining bright, and there was an occasional summer breeze in the air. I settled into the back seat of their Mercedes, and we exchanged our usual cheery good mornings as we set off for Auburn. Years ago we always took what we referred to as the "old way" along Route 5 and down Erie Boulevard West to Westvale through Camillus, Marcellus, and Jordan and then all the way out to Auburn. A leisurely drive to Auburn back then included taking in the sights of huge silos, acres of corn, and dozens of dairy and horse farms. Sunday drives to Auburn were always an opportunity to connect with nature and the farming culture that makes New York State one of the finest. These days the trip is a little less scenic because of the 690 West Highway.

As usual on Sunday drives, Michele had the car radio turned to *Praise,* a Sirius station that plays one gospel song after another. The car was filled with the music of Kirk

Franklin and the Winans. We sang, we swayed our heads left to right, we clapped our hands, and we snapped our fingers as the spirit hit us. I was so looking forward to the brunch that awaited us. We were about thirty minutes away from assorted danish, eggs Benedict, bacon, home fries, creamed chicken with biscuit, and baked ham. I decided that I would taste a bit of everything.

Just outside of Camillus, we came upon a most intriguing sight. There were acres and acres of sunflowers on both sides of Route 5. For miles we gazed upon the splendid beauty of thousands of the golden orbs dotted with chocolate-colored centers. As far as the eye could see, the yellow, daisy-like flowers demanded our attention. One would have thought that we had just discovered the eighth wonder of the world. Our "ohs" and "ahs" and exclamations of "Honey, look!" and "Ma, look!" drowned out the background radio tunes. It was breathtaking. What a wonderful prelude to getting reacquainted with people and times past.

My daughter and son-in-law always sang the praises of the Global Positioning System (GPS) installed in their car. My first-born was satisfied that no matter where she traveled, the GPS got her to her destination. Jokingly, she said that it saved her marriage—no more arguing about what turn to take, having to stop for directions, or driving thirty miles past the right exit. Traveling had become a pleasure with few angry outbursts to boot. Even I became used to hearing the friendly female voice (we affectionately called her "Wanda II") announce our arrivals.

We drove along East Lake Road until we came to the Lakeview Country Club's entrance. Condos, town houses, and new housing developments were sprawled along the way. John turned left onto the winding driveway and drove up to the front doors. Oh, my, how beautiful the grounds looked.

In the distance, we could see golfers teeing off or riding their golf carts to the next hole. Michele and I got out of the car, while John drove off to find a parking space. We stood in front of the club dressed in our Sunday finery—straw hats and all. Meanwhile, several white men playing golf—presumably club members—turned in our direction and acknowledged us with a nod and a smile. We reciprocated the friendly gesture, knowing that they were wondering who we were and what we were doing there. My daughter and I gave each other a knowing glance that without uttering a word signaled, "We're here." Having found a parking space at the far end of the lot, John climbed the winding walkway and joined us as we entered the clubhouse.

The ballroom awaited us just beyond a pair of double doors at the end of the hallway. The smell of breakfast food filled the air. We stood at the registration table for a couple of minutes. There were about eight tables with silver-haired white people seated at them. We looked at them, and they looked at us. Amazing. Even after sixty years, I momentarily had that feeling of being an outsider. Without further ado my daughter proceeded to the nearest table and asked, "Who is in charge here?"

The ladies seated at the registration table appeared taken aback by her question. Someone muttered, "I think Mary Greene is the person you are looking for." Just as we started searching the sea of faces, Mary stood up, walked over, and warmly greeted us. She led us to a free table, where we placed our purses and then made our way to the buffet in the adjoining room. We were famished. The chafing dishes, filled with tasty brunch selections, were a welcomed sight. We filled our plates to our palates' desires and returned to the table with our dishes. Just as we were finishing the last few bites of our meal, a man walked over to our table.

"Joyce, do you remember me?" he asked.

"It has been so long; I am not sure that I do," I replied.

"I am Carl. Carl Campagnola."

"Carl, good to see you. Yes, now I remember. How are you?"

"I am doing pretty good. How are you?"

"Well, I am doing very good. Thank you. This is my daughter Michele and her husband, John, and they drove me here today."

"Nice to meet the two of you. Joyce, I just wanted you to know after all of these years that I was very proud of you for what you did in our senior year. I remember that you refused to take the role of the maid in our senior play."

"You remember that, Carl? I have told that story to my children a million times."

My daughter chimed in.

"I can't believe it. Mom has always told us that story and now I hear you validating what she has recounted as one of the most memorable experiences of her childhood," she piped up.

"Well, I know that your mother refused to be the maid in our senior play. The play was called *Girl Shy*. She wouldn't take the part. As I remember, Penny Rizzo took the part."

"I do not remember who played the part of the maid. I just know that I would not do it. Do you remember that our teacher Mrs. Anderson suggested that I be the usherette at the play?"

"Yes, I remember," said Carl.

My daughter was overjoyed to hear this from someone who

had actually witnessed (and remembered!) the play incident. After all of these years, Carl let me know that I was not alone. At least he, and perhaps a few others in our class, understood why I refused to take the role of the maid. Carl and I knew that I could not and would not demean myself by taking the part of "black servant."

Mrs. Anderson made all the difference in the world to me. She acknowledged my resistance, and she found a way for me to have a respectable role in the senior production.

My parents and I were proud that I would be the usherette at the play. I would usher my classmates, their family and friends, and other attendees to their seats in the auditorium. For the momentous occasion, my parents bought me a full-length powder blue gown with a flattering peplum. I felt like a princess. In fact, my father called me his princess that very evening. On the day of the play, my daddy bought me a white corsage and my mother pinned it to my gown atop my left shoulder. I had asserted myself and those who loved me, liked me, or sympathized with me were proud of me.

Carl Campagnola took me back six decades to a time in my past when I made it clear to everyone, including myself, that I had no desire, interest, or inclination to be showcased as a second-class citizen for my fellow students, their parents, and the faculty to gawk at. Sixty years later Carl helped me to realize that standing by your own convictions cannot only be the cornerstone of one's values, but it can help others to broaden their worldview. That afternoon Carl had simply said that he was proud of me and that Penny Rizzo had taken the part of the maid. In that miraculous moment, I felt that my actions had been valued and vindicated. Other than Mrs. Anderson and my family, someone had taken the time to understand what I went through all those many years ago. Carl Campagnola was my hero that night. I was proud to be with him and my other classmates who attended the sixtieth high school anniversary, as we were seated and positioned for our 2008 class picture.

After our delicious meal and one-on-one conversations, we were all compelled to sing along with each other. A 1948 graduate proudly showcased his accordion and began to play songs that were reminiscent of our youth. We belted out our best notes as we chimed in to the tunes of "Let Me Call You Sweetheart," "Yankee Doodle Dandy," and "East Side West Side." Around 2 p.m. we said our goodbyes and my daughter, her husband, and I headed back to Syracuse. On the drive home that beautiful August afternoon, I thought about my senior year, marveled again at the fields of sunflowers, and reminisced my youth in Auburn, New York.

Joyce Stokes Jones, 1948 (above); Class of 1948's Sixtieth Class Reunion, West High School, Auburn, New York (circa 2008)

CHAPTER TWO

—

Remembrances

L ooking back on my early years in Auburn, I realized that
Negroes, or coloreds, were afforded more opportunities
than people of color were given just a few decades before my
birth. I was raised in a working-class Negro family in Cayuga
County during the 1930s and the late 1940s. It is not talked
about much, but the life for whites and blacks in my hometown
was somewhat typical of the Jim Crow era: whites enjoyed the
privilege of being white, while Negroes understood that having
black skin dictated where you lived, where you worked, and
where you went in life.

My family resided in a brown two-story clapboard house at
59 Chapman Avenue (formerly known as Cornell Street). When
referring to our place, it was called Five-Nine Chapman. When
one drove or walked down South Street opposite the center of
town, our road was the side street to the right, just past the
Emerson house. Still today two stone columns mark the entry
to the street. As a young girl, I remember that my parents
allowed me to take Saturday afternoon strolls down South
Street. No one had to say it, necessarily, but I knew what
everyone else knew—only wealthy white people lived on South
Street and the surrounding cross streets. The Hislops,

Osbornes, Sewards, Emersons, Swifts, Nobles, and others lived a life of luxury in Auburn. Anyone who was anyone lived on South Street. Their opulent homes were enhanced by the sprawling lawns and manicured gardens that were mostly tended to by Negro landscapers.

Most of our family and friends didn't live far from the center of town on Chapman, Garrow, Fitch, and Parker Streets. Auburn was not segregated totally by race. There were not enough Negroes living within the city proper to have a neighborhood exclusively inhabited by blacks. In fact, most blacks lived in integrated neighborhoods with working-class whites. Class and wealth more so than race dictated where people lived in our town. Most colored people worked for hire as teamsters, coachmen, brick makers, barbers, hunters, seamstresses, molders, machinists, servants, cooks, laundresses, nursemaids, landscapers, chauffeurs, whitewashers, and day laborers for wealthy whites. Others of us worked at Mercy Hospital, the Columbian Rope Company, Auburn State Prison, or the Osborne Orphanage.

It was no different for my family. Although my mother, Alida Gaskin Stokes Chaffin, rarely worked outside of the home, my father, Clarence Morgan Stokes, also known as Bobby, was as a teamster who worked most of his adult life for John B. Alger. Alger, a prominent white businessman, owned a draying company. (A dray is a low, sturdy cart that is pulled by a team of draught horses.) My father's position in the company was considered a big deal back then. He was in charge of caring for and training the Morgan horses, as well as matching up drivers, or draymen, with a team of horses that best suited each other. The draying companies were the predecessors to the modern-day trucking companies, and Alger eventually expanded his business into one of the biggest trucking firms in the area.

Not only did my father work for Alger, but Leverette Austin (Buster) Chaffin, a family friend who boarded at our home after his tour in World War II, worked in the trucking division as well. Buster was known to be a great horseman; he handled Alger's Clydesdale horses. I credit my father and Buster for teaching me how to ride horses and for my love of them. Several years after my father's death, my mother and Buster married. He was a kind, considerate, and gentle man. We missed him terribly after his unexpected death from walking pneumonia.

The men in my family, like other men in the neighborhood, were no strangers to hard work. The men worked hard, and many of them drank hard. Mr. Cappiello owned the grocery store across the street from our house. On the weekend, he opened a small area behind the store where the black men from the neighborhood would meet, fraternize, and drink their favorite libations. (Black men were not allowed to patronize the watering holes in town.) At Cappiello's, the men were grateful to have a place where they could relax, release stress, and act a little raucous sometimes. I was grateful to Mr. Cappiello, too, for quite a different reason. He was always warm and friendly to me during my daily visits to buy penny candy, even when it was clear that I had overstayed my welcome. I cherish the memories of him teaching me Italian phrases. My favorite is one that I still say when greeting my children: "Como stai questo oggi?" My kids also like it when I say, "Bene, bene!"

The Negro men in the neighborhood also frequented the Hunter's Club. It was located down the street from our house. Bickerton Richardson originally opened it, and he named it the

Hunter's Club because most of the black men in the area were hunters. Aside from their day jobs, they hunted deer, rabbits, raccoons, woodchucks, and muskrats for food. The club was not only a meeting place where the men were able to gather and talk about the issues of the day, their jobs, and families, but it was a place where they could play cards, shoot craps, and bet on coon and cock fights, too. The Hunter's Club was operational until the 1950s. Robbie Holland and my uncle Phillip Gaskin owned the club for brief periods. Eventually, Robbie Holland reformed the Hunter's Club and established the first black bar on Chapman Avenue. While Cappiello's and the Hunter's Club were sources for alcohol and good times, many of the men were also involved in colored Masonic societies like the Cayuga Lodge 67.F and A.M., Cayuga Lodge 61, and Colored F. and A.M. Nehemiah No. Lodge 28. Much like the majority of working-class blacks and whites after the turn of the twentieth century, my parents only received an elementary school education. They both knew how to read and write, but work, rather than education, was the order of the day. We all understood that education was important; however, the primary competing interest was going to work to make a living wage. Depending on family circumstances, many teenagers left school to work and contribute to the household. As luck would have it, I would continue my education and graduate from high school.

In elementary school, most of my teachers were very nice to me. Few colored children attended Seward Elementary School. Now that I recall, I was the only colored girl and Christopher McCleod was the only colored boy. Many of the other colored children attended school on the west end. Our principal was Ms. Ostrander. My favorite teachers were Ms.

Newcomb, Ms. Anthony, Ms. Murphy, and Ms. Robins. I was only in Ms. Newcomb's class a short time, because she felt that I was beyond kindergarten level and should be promoted to the first grade. I was then promoted to Ms. Anthony's first-grade class. Although I liked school, I sure did miss being at home with my mother, so Ms. Anthony would put me on her lap and comfort me, while she taught the class. One of my fondest memories is of Ms. Murphy. She made me feel very comfortable in her second-grade class, and she gave me twin black dolls for Christmas. I also remember Ms. Robins as a friendly teacher.

One day after class in fourth grade, she told me that she knew my family through my grandmother Mary Gaskin, who worked as a domestic for her family. My least favorite teachers were Ms. Clark and Ms. McGarr. Ms. Clark, a second-grade teacher, would not accept black children in her class. Ms. McGarr wasn't particularly friendly with me, and still to this day, I don't understand her reasoning. Overall, most of my teachers and classmates were kind and accepting.

During junior high school at West High, I distinctly remember my eighth grade teacher growing very angry with me. I decided that I would take out my romance book and finish reading one of the chapters during class time. I was deep into the chapter; it had captured my imagination. Before I knew it, my teacher, whose face had turned beet red, strode swiftly over to my desk and started shouting at the top of his lungs for me to put the book away. I instantly knew that I was in the wrong, and I felt sorry that I had offended him, but I was quite taken aback by what seemed to be an overreaction to a minimal transgression. My parents were none too thrilled to hear about what had happened at school that day.

The book reading episode, coupled with other incidents that were perceived as being racially motivated, prompted my parents and the parents of my good friend Catherine Morehand to send us both to a school where our personal and academic development would be nurtured. At the beginning of the next school year, Catherine and I were train bound for the outskirts of Washington, D.C. We were two new students at the Nannie Burroughs National Trade and Professional School for Women and Girls. It was a private Christian school that promoted a fundamental motto: "Bible, Bath, and Broom." Burroughs whole-heartedly rejected the notion that black women were unclean, uneducated, and unrefined. Underlying the industrial and classical training program, Burroughs insisted on training in morality, religion, and cleanliness. Catherine and I arrived at a six-acre farm in Lincoln Heights, Washington, D.C., in the mid-1940s. Nannie Helen Burroughs was committed to the religious, educational, economic, and political uplifting of black women. Racial pride, respectability, and a strong work ethic were the guiding principles of the trade school. Burroughs and her staff prepared young girls and women to provide for themselves as self-sufficient wage earners and skilled homemakers. Part of the curriculum was that each student was required to take the Negro history class and pass it before graduation. My mother and father believed that by attending the school, I would be fully prepared to enter the work place as a confident professional.

In the beginning, I very much enjoyed attending the school. The teachers were very nice, but strict, and they adhered to the rules set by Principal Burroughs. As time went on, I realized that there were some conditions in my new situation that caused me to feel uncomfortable. On occasion, we traveled into Washington. What stood out vividly in my mind were the "white only" signs. We could go to public places, but only on certain days and during certain hours. That is not to say that these things did not happen in my hometown, because they did. The simple difference was that I was in a new place without the love, safety, and support of my family. I missed them; communication with my family was far and few between—no phone calls at all. I grew quite homesick. My grades did not suffer too much, but I was not motivated to apply my best as a student. Although Catherine and I tried to do everything together and console each other, I wanted to go home. I wanted to go back to where I believed I belonged.

Shortly before I left the school, there was an incident that really impacted me. One day while I was going into a classroom, I happened upon what seemed to be a heated student and teacher exchange. The more heated their verbal exchange got, the more the student became enraged. The student was a little older than me, but I could not believe that she had tried to assault the teacher. The talk around campus was that this particular student was a lesbian. I was too young to really understand what that meant at the time. I was more concerned that she was in a violent rage. I yelled and tried to stop the altercation. She did not appreciate my interference, and I thought that she might try to physically attack me. We later found out that the teacher had rejected the student's romantic advances. Whether that was true or not, my homesickness and this incident served as very good excuses (in my mind) to be brought home immediately. I contacted my parents and voiced my concerns. Knowing me better than anyone else in the world, they reluctantly sent for me to come home. Thinking back on it now, I am sure that my parents did not want me to be unhappy, but I am just as certain that I must have disappointed them and dashed their dream of having me graduate from the distinguished trade school.

I returned to Auburn and completed my high school education at West High. I was glad to be home. I walked the proverbial two miles a day back and forth to school. I did have fun at school, but as I recall, I had a small number of friends. As a black girl, my opportunities for friendship were limited. Most of the kids were white, and as we grew older, some were not anxious to be acquainted with a colored girl. While I often thought about how race played a major role in interracial friendships, it did not diminish my self-worth as a person. I had spent enough time at the Nannie Burroughs School to know that no matter where I was or who I had a relationship with, whether white or black, I was worthy of dignity and respect. I do not think my time in high school was much different from other black American girls who attended a mostly white school. My time at West High was rather typical for that of any black girl growing up in 1940s Auburn. There were a few memorable events, too.

In the eleventh grade, I was stunned when my history teacher Mr. Williams spoke about Aunt Harriet. He was very intelligent and knowledgeable about American history. He also gave me the sense that he knew a great deal about the history of Negroes in this country, but he was not free to discuss it. He did, however, speak briefly about a local Negro woman of notoriety. I was proud and honored that day to hear him talk about my great-great-grandaunt Harriet Tubman as a special person for the work she did to free slaves. And then there was our senior play. I wanted to be a cheerleader my senior year, but the captain of the cheerleading squad would have none of it. She suggested that I be the maid in our senior play. I was adamant that I would not portray a maid in that year's play or any other year. My twelfth grade teacher, Ms. Anderson, came to the rescue. She completely understood why I would not volunteer to be the maid. She suggested that I be the usherette instead. The day of the senior play, I felt like Cinderella. Some would have said that I was the center of attention. I was not so lucky for my senior prom. I had always dreamt about going, as most girls do. It was not that I didn't have someone to escort me; one of the Freeman boys wanted to take me. When I told my mother the name of the young man who had asked me to prom, she told me to politely decline the invitation. I was shocked. As it turned out, he was a distant relative, and my mother frowned upon our being seen as an item. I was very disappointed to miss one of the highlights of my senior year, but there was nothing I could do to change her mind. My high school years were not always the best of times, yet they shaped who I am, and best of all, I did graduate.

Alida Gaskin Stokes Chaffin, great-grandniece of Harriet Tubman, with son Robert in front of 59 Chapman Avenue

Clarence Morgan Stokes with his team of Morgan Horses at the John B. Alger stables

CHAPTER THREE

—

Family Tree

I n the 1940s, I spent much of my free time at the Harmon Playground and the Booker T. Washington Community Center. Although the neighborhood was integrated, the colored children mostly frequented both places. I was very active and athletic. The Harmon Playground was my favorite place to play. I was one of the best jacks players around, and I enjoyed competing in jacks tournaments and running the 25- and 50-yard dashes. I wasn't the best swimmer, but I was a pretty darn good pitcher and first baseman on the softball team. I fondly remember reporting for the Harmon Playground paper. My reports always began the same way: "Hello, again. This is Joyce Stokes." In the summer of 1943, there was so much going on in our playground community—softball games, a horseshoe tournament, and the embroidery, handcrafts, and fine articles that the girls made for the annual gathering. There was always fun to be had at the playground.

During my youth, I also regularly attended the Booker T. Washington Community Center. The center was conveniently located just down the street from our quaint two-story home on Chapman and directly across the road from the playground.

I was about six- or seven-years-old when Eleanor Hardy, the center's new director, moved to Auburn from Virginia. She was very tall and rather light complexioned. She wore no makeup, had dark, medium-length hair, and dressed rather plainly. Mrs. Hardy always had a smile on her face, and she was extremely friendly with everyone. She had a very distinct quality to her laugh; it was somewhat musical.

One day after school, I rushed home to check in with Mamma, before running down the street to the center. I wanted to make sure that I was on time for story hour. I ran up the front steps, opened the door, and moved quickly through a small hallway. I flung my coat onto the next available hook. Rushing, as usual, I scooted my way to my favorite seat, which was located under a large picture of an older Negro woman. Her wrinkled, bony, and strong hands were gently folded on her lap. The dark lady in the portrait wore an old, white scarf around her neck. Wisps of crinkly hair peaked out from under her bandana. Her dark, penetrating eyes seemed to engulf me. I was excited and waited patiently to see what important person I'd soon learn about that day.

Mrs. Hardy welcomed us and waited for every child to be seated before she began to tell the story of a slave woman who ran away from her master in the South. This brave Negro woman also helped hundreds of other Negroes escape from slavery. She was known for assisting anyone who needed her help. Mrs. Hardy mentioned that this heroine made her home in Fleming, New York, right down the road, just outside of the Auburn city line. That was the first time that I had ever heard a story about a slave. Mrs. Hardy pointed to the picture hanging above me and said, "That's the woman I'm talking about, and her name is Harriet Tubman."

After story hour ended, I dashed home to tell my mother about the courageous lady in the painting. I ran back through the small dining room into the kitchen where she was preparing supper, and I began telling Mamma the story of the woman who had escaped slavery and led other slaves to freedom. Mamma did not seem to be surprised. Apparently, this was common knowledge to her and others in the family, but it was news to me. Mamma continued making her bread pudding. She pushed the pan into the oven and coolly said to me, "That's your aunt." I was stunned by the family revelation. I was pleasantly surprised, proud, and mystified all at once. Mamma simply smiled and began to tell me more about our famous relative, who (unbeknownst to me) everyone fondly called Aunt Harriet. I was not aware then how this family connection would later become the impetus for my quest to unearth our family's ties to the greatest heroine of our times. And it took me many years to discover the exact nature of our kinship.

If I knew as a young girl what I know now, I would have used more of my time and visits with family and friends to inquire about slavery, survival, challenges, and triumphs. They held the keys to our past. I would have wanted to hear more of their personal stories. My research has only scraped the surface of their lives, only peeling away a fraction of what remembrances, family interviews, historical accounts, and state documents can do to reconstruct them. On my way to finding our family connection to Harriet Tubman, I uncovered a patchwork of details that allowed me to piece together things that I did not know and to create a tapestry of our lives. I realized that the people closest to me had a relationship with the greatest heroine in American History. My mother's parents, her siblings, her husband, and close friends were the very same people that Harriet Tubman loved and called family. With that said, let me share my most vivid memories of those who tolerated the sometimes pestering of a young girl who seemingly had nothing better to do.

My mother, Lyda, was a beautiful Christian woman. Her dark brown eyes were deeply set in her golden-colored face. Her near waist-length black hair was braided and fashioned into a crown atop her head. Her natural beauty was simply enhanced by the makeup she wore. It was always applied perfectly—not too much and not too little. She was partial to the colors pink, mauve, and lavender. From her lipstick to her fingernails to her spiked high heels, she was aglow in her favorite colors. All who knew and loved her, including my husband, Harry, who had great respect for her, lovingly referred to her as the Pink Lady. My mother was also a very talented woman. She loved music and taught tap dancing. She played our upright Baldwin piano religiously, and she spent hours writing music and composing lyrics. My mother was never as pleased as she was on the day that she had a recording made of one of her songs, "Lock Up My Heart."

Lock Up My Heart

I'm gonna lock up my heart and throw the key away
I'm gonna lock up my heart forever and a day
My honey left me, and I'm bluer than blue
There's only one thing left to do
I'm gonna lock up my heart and throw the key away

In my mind's eye, my mother was the best. She took care of our every need. Each morning before school, she made sure that we were dressed properly and ate a good breakfast that kept us nourished until we walked home at noon for lunch break. Our lunch menu would often consist of lettuce, tomato, and mayonnaise sandwiches with a side of rhubarb, apples, blueberries, or cherries for dessert. My favorites were peanut butter and jelly, or bologna sandwiches. We would usually have milk, iced tea, or lemonade as a beverage. A delicious supper was always ready and on the table at five o'clock. My mom was not only a wonderful homemaker and a very good cook, but she was a very creative person, too.

Mamma was also involved in her church and the community. She was particularly honored and proud when she was inducted into the Harriet Tubman Booster Club. My mother, with my father's help, made every attempt to help others. As I recall, they often assisted Mr. Allen, our next-door neighbor. He suffered from a seizure disorder, and he would occasionally fall and hit his head. His wife was not able to bear the situation and left him. Once, he slammed his head against his living room window. My mother and father swiftly made their way to his side to help him recover. Mr. Allen was forever grateful to them.

My mother and father were also known to open their doors to Negro men who had been released from the Auburn prison. My parents knew that these men would have difficulties reentering society with a prison record. With a delicious homemade meal in their bellies (prepared by my mother), counsel from my father, and encouragement from the both of them, the men departed from Five-Nine Chapman ready to create a new life. Mamma and Daddy provided us kids, other family members, neighbors, and friends with a safe haven where we all felt their love and compassion.

As I recall, I would play outside everyday after school while watching for my father to turn onto our street from the laneway down the road as he made his daily walk home from a hard day's work. Daddy was known to be quite a fast walker. Some say he was also pretty good at softball and could outrun the best of them. My father never learned to drive, so he did not have much use for cars. Our car was driven by Mamma. Daddy relied upon his Morgan horses George and Dan. He delivered goods and supplies to area businesses, including the Osborne Orphanage and Auburn State Prison. Many businesses relied on him to keep their operations going. Neither rain nor snow slowed the work of good ol' George, Dan, and Daddy. The deliveries were made on time every day. The days were long and the work was hard.

My father was also hired by my high school to take the students on hayrides and sleigh rides. During my senior year, he took my class on a winter sleigh ride. My heart melted with pride when I saw him waiting to board us. Other families in the community hired him to till their gardens in the spring, so that the garden beds would be ready to take seed for the following seasonal harvests. He could not have done any of it without George and Dan. I truly believe they were his best friends. He claimed they were the best horses around.

This proclamation was confirmed by the number of first-prize ribbons he and his horses won at pulling contests during the 1930s and 1940s. On one such occasion, the local newspaper headlined a story about a recent win. It reported that the Auburn team was the winner and major honors were given in the heavyweight division to John B. Alger's team. Bobby Stokes, a well-known Auburn colored teamster, drove the team of horses. The Alger team pulled 2,750 pounds for 27½ feet. My father was proud of the work they did together.

I should mention here that my father married our mother

after his first wife, Leola Dale, died. They had five children together: Elmer, Augustus (Gus), Ida, Lillian, and Earl (he died in infancy). After the death of my father's first wife and the death of their infant son, he continued to care for his children and his aging father, John, in the family homestead at 61 Cornell Street. His mother, Lucy, had since passed away.

When my father married my mother, they leased the house next door at 59 Chapman, and it was there where they raised the children they had together. For some time, my half-siblings lived with us until they were old enough to be out on their own. My parents lost their first child, Marilyn, to childhood disease. Upon her death, the chubby, curly haired child was buried in the same plot as Leola and Earl. Later, my parents would also lose in childhood John Austin and Richard Thomas.

To my surprise, I learned that, although my dad was born in Aurora, New York, as a child, he and his parents, John and Lucy, moved to 56 Cornell Street. He was raised there with his siblings, Mabel, Edwin, Willie, Irene, Roy, and Glen. This street actually later became Chapman Avenue—the center of hearth and home for many black families in Auburn during the early 1900s.

One evening after supper, my father seated himself in his favorite armchair in the living room. He propped his legs up on his footstool and smoked one of his choice wooden pipes. Daddy had a full face, and his skin was the color of damp earth. His hair was black, curly, and close cropped. My dad had a short and muscular build. He was a friendly person, but most people knew him to be somewhat reserved. On this occasion, he was listening to his favorite radio show *Mr. Keene, Tracer of Lost Persons.* Everyone in the house knew that not a word was to be spoken while Daddy's show was on. He leaned back comfortably and large, bluish-white clouds of smoke rose out of his pipe, as he listened intently to the adventures of Mr. Keene. Once the program ended and he had that familiar look of satisfaction on his face, my dad told me about his personal encounters with Aunt Harriet. He explained that he and his teenage neighborhood friends frequently took Aunt Harriet on errands. They would take her by horse and buggy from her South Street Road home in Fleming to the local merchants for various goods and supplies. The young men would also take her to visit family members, neighbors, and her prominent white acquaintances. Oftentimes, my father and his friends would be in mid-conversation with Harriet during these carriage rides and they would notice that she was not responding. She appeared to have fallen fast asleep. No matter how much they tried, she was unable to be stirred; yet when she did awaken, she continued the conversation right where she left off. It seemed as if she had no recollection that the involuntary blackout had occurred at all. The young men learned that this condition was caused by a serious head injury that Aunt Harriet had suffered as a teenager. In a fit of rage, an irate overseer inflicted the skull-crushing blow. The injury scarred her and left her with this debilitating malady that remained with her until death. Anyone that knew her well was aware of her spells.

My older sister, Hazel, and I were very close. She was very protective of Bobby and me. She, too, had a creative streak. If she had her druthers, she would find a quiet spot in the house or the yard and draw for hours. She impressed everyone with her artwork. She was a gifted artist. She graduated from Erie Community College and attended school for graphics and design, and she later studied painting under the tutelage of the famed artist Charles Birchfield. For a period, Hazel also established and maintained an art studio in Buffalo, New York.

Hazel was very popular and very pretty. One could not have asked for a better sister. She was my role model. Although she was a few years older than me, she understood me, and she took the time to answer my silly questions and comfort me when needed. My sister, mother, and I had a very special bond. And I tried to be like them in any way that I could. Hazel, along with my mother, helped me to understand what it meant to be a young lady. While Hazel lovingly took me under her wing, we were both under the watchful eye of our mother.

Hazel eventually met and married Joseph Martin from Martinsville, Virginia. She was a wonderful mom, and she and her husband made a home in Buffalo with their four surviving children, Naomi (Candy), Josephine and Joyce (twins), and Ernestine (Tina). Joseph Jr. and JoAnn, their first set of twins, passed away in infancy. What I remember most about my brother-in-law Joe is that he loved to tease people—and I believe that I was one of his favorite victims. I'll admit, at first I was a little intimidated by him. Yet the more confident I became, I think I gave him a run for his money.

Similar to our mother, Hazel brought the love of God, family, and community into the heart and lives of her family. In mid-life she found salvation in Jesus Christ. In Auburn, she was a member of the Thompson A.M.E. Zion Church, and in Buffalo, she received the Lord Jesus Christ and became a member of the St. Paul A.M.E. Zion Church. There she was consecrated as a deaconess and served as the president of the Pastor's Aide Society. She was a member of the Women's Home Society and the Home Missions. As a charter member, she was moved to the Varick Metropolitan A.M.E. Zion Church. There she taught the junior Sunday school, was director of children, the superintendent of Buds of Promise, and advisor to the Youth Builders and the Young Adult Missionary Society. For a dozen years, she was the president of the deaconess board. In the last days of her life, Hazel sang her way through the gates of heaven.

My brother Bobby, although he never married, was very involved in the lives of his nieces and nephews. At seventeen he enlisted in the Army and served in World War II. He returned home after his military service. He was not changed as much by the time he spent in the armed services as he was by the premature death of his best friend, Eugene Richardson. Bobby followed our sister to Buffalo, where he worked for the American Aluminum Magnesium Company and Sisters Hospital. At the hospital, he was a supervisor in the housekeeping division. Sadly, my brother also died prematurely at the age of forty-seven. My mother, sister, and I, were devastated by his sudden death. His passing left a tremendous void in our lives. We just could not believe that Bobby had left us.

My mother's brother Richard and his wife, Bertha, lived a distance away on Bradford Street. Prior to moving there, they lived with my mother's brother Phillip and his wife, Myrtle, at 77 Chapman. We did not visit Uncle Richie, Aunt Bertha, and their family much after their move to Bradford Street, because they lived quite a distance away and back then people did not have cars. As I remember, they had three children: Mary Belle, Justine, and Chester. Aunt Bertha had been married previously. She had three children from that union. The children were Uncle Richie's stepchildren. We all enjoyed our time together when we were able to visit. Later on, Justine married John Copes and lived in Auburn. Mary married Timothy Chaffin and they lived in Buffalo. As a young man, Chester resided in Philadelphia.

Uncle Phil was a gardener and Aunt Myrtle was a homemaker for the most part. I recall that she pierced my ears. Uncle Phil had a great sense of humor and was famous for saying things like "criminey sakes" or "cracker dust" when he didn't agree with something that had been said. I also remember that my uncle and our distant relative Charlie Stewart would hold long conversations across their back porches.

When we went to visit Uncle Phil and Aunt Myrtle, the adults usually sat in their kitchen. Of course I was not allowed to sit and listen to the grown ups' conversation, so I usually found a way to busy myself in the next room or outside. My cousins Laberta and Phillip, Jr. were a little older than me, but we were very close. As youngsters, one of my fondest memories is of playing jacks with them. Laberta went on to work for General Electric in Auburn and Saunder's Photographic and Taylor's Instrument in Rochester. Phillip was a military man and one of the best saxophonists around. He married Elizabeth Copes, a WAC who received an honorable discharge from the Army, and settled in Auburn where he worked for the Columbian Rope Company. Laberta married Henry "Buddy" Greenlea, Jr., and they lived in Rochester with their daughter Tanya.

My mother's sister Jennie (Jeanette) and her husband, Guy Copes, lived on Parker Street. What I remember most about Aunt Jennie was that she had a caring and affectionate nature. When my mother and I used to visit, she would have prepared a light lunch. She always seemed to enjoy feeding us. At first, we would sit in her living room and chat, and then she would take us into her kitchen to eat. To me, the food was the best part of the visit. Now my Uncle Guy, he loved to sing, and buddy he could belt out a tune. He had a wonderful baritone voice. My aunt and uncle had five children: Jeannette, Arlene, Pauline, Geraldine, and William (he died after his service in World War II.)

Jeanette was first married to Guernsey Bennett. Her second husband was Henry Johnson. Arlene was married first to Charles Phillip Johnson. Her second husband was Walter Breedlove. Pauline married Chauncey Johnson, and Geraldine married Milton Daniels. William married Ernestine Sherman. Aunt Jennie and Uncle Guy were blessed with many grandchildren, great-grandchildren, and great-great-grandchildren.

My mother's aunt Martha was the sister of her mother, Mary. Even those of my generation referred to her simply as Aunt Martha. If memory serves me well, she was of short stature and was the color of a Hershey's chocolate bar. She usually had her hair wrapped in a dark brown kerchief. When I see pictures of Aunt Harriet, it seems to me that Aunt Martha resembled her.

Aunt Martha was married to William Chaney. They had a daughter named Gertrude Lee, who sadly died at nine years of age in a massive fire at their home at 21 Union Avenue. Gertie suffered terrible burns and contracted tetanus. She was taken to the home of her great-grandaunt Harriet Tubman, where Harriet, her mother, Martha, and other women folk in the family cared for her. It seemed that little Gertrude would recover, but she took a turn for the worst and passed away.

In my youth, I do not remember Uncle William. He passed away when I was very young. I do remember Aunt Martha. Her small house on Chapman was set back with the side of the house facing Forgette Lane. She would take me to the room near her kitchen. I would be seated on a rough-hewn wooden bench, and she would hand me a stalk or two of reddish-green rhubarb to eat. I always looked forward to getting them. She was somewhat reserved, but very kind.

There was one distinctive feature about Aunt Martha that I remember as plain as day; her arm below her elbow was missing. She was working at the Osborne Orphanage when her arm got caught in the washing machine wringer. She would wear her blouse or dress sleeve shortened on that arm, or sometimes tied it at the bottom. Even with the injury, she went about her business with not much ado about it. It had become part of her life, and she learned to cope with it. After her husband's death, she took care of herself without any assistance.

As Aunt Martha grew older, she required a little more help from Alida and Phil, her niece and nephew. Her older sister Mary had since died, and they were the only family living closest to her. She began to wander and was often found sitting on a bench on South Street Road. She was trying to recapture her childhood and made frequent visits to her second home at her great-aunt Harriet Tubman Davis' house. When my mother and Uncle Phil found her missing, they knew where she would be. They would walk out there together, and they would take her back home. Eventually, Aunt Martha came to live with us; her bedroom was adjacent to our living room. When death was near, she was taken to Mercy Hospital where she died.

I also remember Alida Stewart Johnson. She and my

mother shared the same first name. Alida's family was descendant from Aunt Harriet's brother William Henry. Alida and Charlie Stewart were brother and sister, and they lived next door to Uncle Phil in a house that faced Garrow Street. Their brother Clarence "Dye" Stewart lived on Parker Street. As a child, I used to visit the Stewarts, and Mrs. Johnson would give me little snacks.

When she was ailing later in life, she called me into her sick room and told me that I was a nice little girl. We spent some time together; she made me feel very special.

Mrs. Johnson was the mother of Gladys Stewart Bryant. Gladys married Henry Bryant and they had a daughter named Judy. Judy and I were around the same age. At that time, they lived on Garrow Street. The family eventually moved to Skaneateles. But I must note that when Gladys heard that I was involved in researching my family history and our ties to Aunt Harriet, she went into her archives and presented me with a picture of my great-grandmother Ann Marie Stewart Elliott. I will be forever grateful, as it was so very important to my research.

Then, there were cousins Stella Phillips and George Minks. They were my grandfather Phillip Gaskin's niece and nephew. Their mothers, Rose Gaskin Phillips and Mary Naomi Gaskin Minks, were my grandfather's sisters. As young people, they were raised in Sherwood, not far from the farmland that their grandparents Richard and Mary Ann Gaskin owned. Stella and George were my mother's first cousins and my second cousins. As adults, they moved to Auburn and lived on Fitch Avenue. They were much older than me. We seldom had the chance to visit them, as everyone was busy living their day-to-day lives.

Of course, that did not stop me from making my rounds. I

always enjoyed visiting with Mrs. Smith. She was one of my favorites. She lived down the street, but her house was several yards up. In the summer, I found myself on her front porch. She would go to the garden and bring back a basket of string beans. She showed me how to open the green sack and release the beans. Together we would place them in another basket and snack on the fresh, raw vegetables. When we were finished having our fill, Mrs. Smith would go to her kitchen and cook them for dinner, and I would make my way home.

Mrs. Smith was also a very good friend of my grandmother and Aunt Harriet. Mrs. Smith and Grandmother Mary Gaskin were both named in Aunt Harriet's last will and testament as heirs to her estate. She was a good friend of the family. Her husband, Reverend Charles Smith, was the chaplain at the John Brown Home for the Aged, which was founded by Harriet Tubman Davis. Aunt Harriet and Rev. Smith knew each other from their Civil War days. Mrs. Frances Smith and her husband were very close to Aunt Harriet, and at her passing, they were devastated to have her no longer.

There was also Mrs. Cook. She was friendly with my grandmother. She lived a few doors down from the Stewarts on Garrow Street and around the corner from my grandmother. She was an older white woman who was a friend of the family. She and my grandmother chatted about the fact that, as a young girl, I had high blood pressure. Mrs. Cook told my grandmother how to lower the pressure; I was to be given the juice of half a lemon in a half cup of hot water every day before breakfast. As far as I know, the pressure went down. I don't know what Dr. Copeland would have said about this home remedy, but we were happy that it worked.

Another one of my most vivid childhood memories

involved the murder of Lizzie Dale. She was a neighbor who
lived down the street. To the best of my recollection, the
horrendous incident occurred on New Year's Eve—my
birthday. Apparently, there was a grave shooting and Lizzie was
fatally wounded. Lizzie's husband, Jimmy, was shot, as well,
but he survived. The murderer was a local man who was
enraged that Lizzie was committed to another man. It was a
crime of passion. The whole neighborhood was devastated.
The murderer knew that he had committed a terrible act, and
he returned to his home to wait for the police to arrest him. He
was convicted and served his time and later returned to the
Auburn community.

I was a grade school student at the time. The whole episode
was hard to believe, and to think that we would never see
Lizzie again was unbelievable. I was reminded daily of the
tragic incident, as I walked past the crime scene four times a
day going back and forth from home to Seward School. I was
frightened. The sight of Lizzie's blood on the tattered curtains
that flapped through the open window on the second floor
nauseated me. For weeks I tried to shield my eyes from looking
at the evidence of the heinous crime. Eventually, those bloody
curtains were removed and the window was closed. My sense of
safety and security was slowly restored.

Looking back on my childhood, I find that my family's
story was really no better or worse than other people's. We had
to take the good with the bad. For the most part, the bad times
were given short shrift, because black folks were too busy
trying to live life in the present. It was all about moving
forward and living one day at a time. The good times were
cherished, and the difficult times were minimized, if dwelt
upon at all. Compared to slavery and the memory of the recent

past, they had much for which to be grateful. Love of God, family, and compassion for others were the values by which to live. As a young girl, I witnessed how these values played an important role in building relationships with our family, friends, and neighbors. More importantly, I believe that Aunt Harriet and our ancestors would be pleased to know that we took care of one another the best that we could; there is no higher mission in life.

During the early 1970s, I was the producer/director of a segment called *Black History Week* at Channel 24, a local public broadcasting station. I developed a historical program on the life and times of Harriet Tubman, conductor of the Underground Railroad, and our family connection. I interviewed a number of relatives, including my mother and Uncle Phillip, who shared their memories of Aunt Harriet.

I interviewed my mother and her brother Phil, both in their sixties, in his home. The home, now recognized by the National Historic Register, was originally owned by their parents, Mary Elliott Gaskin and Phillip Gaskin, Sr. Mary and Phillip settled in a small house at 56 Garrow Street during the early years of their marriage and then moved their growing family to 34 Union Avenue. Later, they moved to 69½ Cornell Street, where they lived for several years before leasing their home at 77 Cornell Street before it was renamed to Chapman Avenue. In 1927, the Gaskins eventually purchased the home they leased from Rachel and Thomas Belt, other free blacks. Twenty years later, their son Phillip acquired the property through a public auction after paying arrears in the collection of taxes.

We were seated in the small, but well-appointed, kitchen at 77 Chapman. Mamma began by telling me that she remembered taking walks with her mother, Mary, and her grandaunt Harriet. They walked from Aunt Harriet's South Street Road home to the family home on Chapman Avenue. My mother was a young child, about four- or five-years-old, and during these walks, she remembered passing the Quill Dairy Farm, which was also located on South Street Road. As the three of them walked along that familiar route, my mother, her mother, and Aunt Harriet would half-glance at the cows, horses, and other farm animals along the way. They always knew when they were coming upon the Quill property because of the pungent farm odors that filled the air. My mother recalled walking past the farm on one occasion, and she said to her aunt "I want that pony over there." Offering her little great-grandniece a freshly picked apple from the many apple trees on her property—one of Aunt Harriet's favorite fruits—the elder woman promised to get a horse for her one day. Of course my mother believed her aunt Harriet. However, the sad truth was that at that point in her life, the aging heroine in our family had very little money to spend on such things. Although my mother's childhood fantasy was never fulfilled, the promise was well intentioned, and sadly, her aunt Harriet died just a couple of years later.

Uncle Phil listened intently to his sister's recollections. When she finished, he was ready to tell what he remembered about his great-grandaunt. My uncle was in his seventies. His six-foot frame leaned forward, as he folded his long teak wood-colored arms and rested them on the table. He was a very handsome man, the kind of man who had a mischievous spirit and was always joking around. His hair was thick, crinkly, and close cropped. As usual, he was casually dressed in a long-sleeved, plaid shirt and slacks. He began his recollections by telling me about Aunt Harriet's ability to walk without sound.

He described how the family would be gathered around the supper table and without any notice, Aunt Harriet would suddenly appear in their midst. They never heard her footsteps, or the usual sounds of footsteps trampling the leaves, twigs, and grass alongside the house. She had the extraordinary skill of walking without being detected. Uncle Phil claimed that she acquired this craft during her Underground Railroad and Civil War days. He spoke proudly about how his famous aunt served valiantly as a military leader, a spy, a scout, and a nurse in the Civil War, by order of Governor John A. Andrew of Massachusetts.

The sharing of these stories inspired me to conduct further research on my great-great-grandaunt Harriet Tubman. My investigation led me to the discovery of the capture and purchase of Aunt Harriet's grandmother Modesty, who we believe was born in Ghana, West Africa. My study also revealed the relationships between family members, slave masters, and mistresses. My search provided me with insight into their lives as slaves on plantations on the Eastern Shore of Maryland. Furthermore, I uncovered Aunt Harriet's father's influence on her desire to escape from slavery, as well as her courageous efforts to lead her family and other Negroes to freedom. I learned of the depth of her participation in the Civil War, her acquaintance with the Women's Suffrage Movement, and her lifetime commitment to helping the needy. The foregoing has allowed me to construct the following story on Aunt Harriet's heritage within the context of the Green Ross Stewart Elliott Gaskin Stokes lineage and her heroic accomplishments, while delving into the impact of race and color on both of our lives.

Harriet Tubman's death marked the end of the historic abolition era in the United States of America. I learned that my grandmother Mary Elliott Gaskin and her family attended the funeral of one of the greatest historical figures of our country. I was filled with pride to know that my mother, Alida, as a gifted and creative eight-year-old, also attended Harriet's funeral. My mother and her mother witnessed the greatness of a woman who served her country with distinction. Harriet Tubman Davis was buried with full military honors at Fort Hill Cemetery in Auburn. The likes of this heroine would not ever be known again. The former slave turned abolitionist and military general transitioned to the other side, in full glory, to meet her maker.

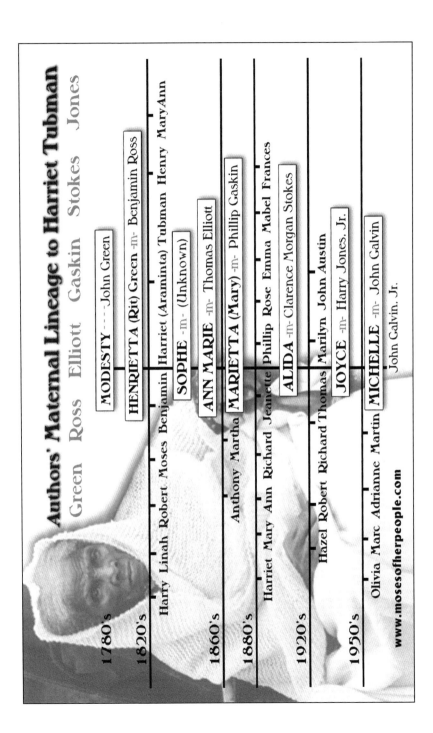

Authors' Maternal Lineage to Harriet Tubman

Green   Ross   Elliott   Gaskin   Stokes   Jones

1780's
MODESTY ---John Green

1820's
HENRIETTA (Rit) Green -m- Benjamin Ross

Harry Linah Robert Moses Benjamin Harriet (Araminta) Tubman Henry MaryAnn

SOPHE -m- (Unknown)

1860's
ANN MARIE -m- Thomas Elliott

1880's
MARIETTA (Mary) -m- Phillip Gaskin

Anthony Martha

Phillip Rose Emma Mabel Frances

1920's
ALIDA -m- Clarence Morgan Stokes

Harriet Mary Ann Richard Jeanette

Hazel Robert Richard Thomas Marilyn John Austin

1950's
JOYCE -m- Harry Jones. Jr.

MICHELLE -m- John Calvin

Olivia Marc Adrianne Martin

John Calvin. Jr.

www.mosesofherpeople.com

Marietta (Mary) Elliott Gaskin, grandniece of Harriet Tubman (above);
Phillip Gaskin, married Harriet Tubman's grandniece Marietta
Elliott. They are the parents of Alida Gaskin Stokes Chaffin.

Hazel Stokes Martin, great-great-grandniece of Harriet Tubman (above); Clarence Morgan Stokes was married to Alida Gaskin Stokes Chaffin and is the author's father.

Richard Gaskin, brother of Alida Gaskin and great-grandnephew of
Harriet Tubman, and wife, Bertha (above); Phillip Gaskin, brother of
Alida, great-grandnephew of Harriet Tubman, World War I veteran

Aunt Jeanette (Jennie) Gaskin Copes, sister of Alida Gaskin and great-grandniece of Harriet Tubman, and husband Guy Copes; Leverette "Buster" Austin Chaffin, second husband of Alida Stokes, World War II veteran

CHAPTER FOUR

—

Green Ross Stewart Elliott
Gaskin Lineage

I n short order, I became the family historian. Reams of handwritten notes and typed writings, yellowed newspaper clippings, photos and documents in plastic coverings, tons of books, bulging file cabinets, and miles of travel consumed much of my free time during the past 35 years. These are all a testament to my insatiable desire to study and research every lead, document, fact, and family lore to confirm my family connection to Harriet Tubman Davis, the famed conductor of the Underground Railroad. Undoubtedly, all roads led to my maternal grandmother, nee Marietta Elliott. Mary, as she was called, was one of Harriet Tubman's many nieces and nephews among many grandnieces and grandnephews. Although Harriet married twice, she had no biological children of her own, but she was known to have a deep fondness for children.

My grandmother Mary was one of her favorites, mostly because she was the first-born daughter of Harriet's closest niece, Ann Marie. Ann Marie was the daughter of Sophe— Harriet's sister who was sold by their master to live out the rest of her life enslaved in the Deep South. The master forced Sophe to abandon her infant daughter, leaving Ann Marie motherless and in the care of her grandparents Rit and Ben Ross. Along with Rit and Ben, Harriet, Harry, Benjamin, Robert, Mary Ann, Henry, and Moses helped their parents to nurture their sister's child. They had been through this same tragedy before when the master sold their other sister, Linah. Linah was forced to leave her two daughters, Harriet and Kessiah, on the plantation without her motherly love, care, and rearing. Although this separation was devastating to the family, it was not an unusual occurrence. The master rarely lost a night's sleep thinking about the upheaval and travesty that he caused.

As a young escaped slave, Ann Marie lived with her uncle James and aunt Catherine in St. Catharines, Canada, under the assumed moniker of Martha Stewart. Harriet's brother Benjamin assumed the name of James Stewart, and his wife, Jane, took the name Catherine Stewart. Other than Harriet Tubman, who took the last name of her husband, the Ross family that relocated to Canada as escaped slaves changed their first names and assumed Stewart (the sir name of a plantation owner) as their last name. John Trevillion Stewart, a shipbuilder, owned slaves, leased slaves, and lost his fortune after he freed his slaves. The Rosses had a very good relationship with Stewart, so they took his name as free people. After James' death, Martha, Catherine, and Catherine's daughter Hester and son Elijah, moved to Fleming to live with Harriet. Catherine Stewart later married Andrew Winslow, and they had a son together named Albert.

When Martha (Ann Marie) left Canada and moved to Fleming, she decided to take back her birth name. Shortly thereafter, Ann Marie married Thomas Elliott, a former slave of the renowned Dover Eight. As a young girl, she knew Thomas while living on the Brodess Plantation.

In 1866, Ann Marie and Thomas had their first child, Marietta (Mary), who was the first baby to be born in Harriet's clapboard frame house on South Street Road. Mary's birth was followed by the births of her sister Martha Jeanette and brother Anthony. Mary and her parents lived with Harriet for a couple of years. The Elliotts were not the only relatives or friends who boarded at the seven-acre Tubman Davis homestead; Harriet Tubman was known to shelter many freedom seekers that settled in Auburn or nearby townships and those passing through to Canada. Even though the Elliotts eventually moved to Thornton Street, where Martha Jeanette and Anthony were born, and later moved into a frame house they built on Union Avenue, they always considered Aunt Harriet's house on the Auburn-Fleming line as home.

My great-grandparents Ann Marie and Thomas Elliott escaped from slavery on the Eastern Shore of Maryland, found freedom in St. Catharines, Canada, and then made Cayuga County, New York, their home. From the ramshackle shanties of Southern plantations to the two-story framed dwelling in Fleming to their own home built at 31 Union Street, the Elliott family lived as free blacks. And the taste of freedom was delectable.

Quite like other young colored women, their daughter Mary found domestic work outside of her family home at the age of fifteen. She was fortunate to be hired as a servant for the Halsey family in the village of Mentz, Cayuga County. Soon after her employment there, she met a young laborer named Phillip Gaskin who had worked for several years in Avon, New York. Phillip moved back into his childhood home with his parents, Richard and Mary Gaskin, and his sisters in Ledyard,

Joyce Stokes Jones and Michele Jones Galvin

Cayuga County. After their courtship, Mary and Phillip married in the winter of 1881 at the A.M.E. Church in Auburn. The newly married couple also settled into a small home at 56 Garrow Street. There, they began to raise their growing family. Their eleven children were Harriet, Ann, Mary, Mabel, Richard, Jeanette, Rose, Emma, Frances, Phillip, and Alida. As the family grew, the Gaskins moved to 34 Union Avenue off of South Street Road. Years later, as the grown children married and moved outside of the household, the Gaskins and their three youngest children, Rose, Phillip, and Alida, moved into 69½ Chapman Street. Phillip Gaskin, Sr. made a good living as a self-employed teamster. He delivered goods to vendors and businesses by horse and wagon. He was in a very good financial position to lease, and subsequently purchase, their final home at 77 Chapman Avenue from family friends Thomas and Rachel Belt. The Belts were escaped slaves from Maryland who settled in Auburn, and their descendants remain friends with the descendants of the Gaskins still today.

Auburn was a quaint place, and like many small cities of the day in Central New York, old wealthy families flourished, family farms thrived, businesses succeeded, and new houses sprang up everywhere. The Gaskins, like many Negroes with local family roots, or coloreds who were new arrivals from Canada or the South, found a life of freedom in the hometown of William H. Seward, the former secretary of state under President Abraham Lincoln. Free Negroes and former slaves either experienced or heard through the grapevine that the Quakers, Whigs, and other abolitionists welcomed them, and they could find work in the homes and businesses of white owners and make a living wage.

My memories of my grandparents Mary and Phillip are few

and shadowy in my mind's eye. My grandfather worked for more than fifty years as a teamster. He was a tall man with a slight build. He had the most beautiful deep brown skin. His chiseled features and high cheekbones made for a very handsome gentleman. My most vivid memory of him is one of him standing in our living room doorway smiling down at me. I also remember my grandmother Mary as a warm and very kind person. She usually wore her hair parted down the middle with the sides pulled back and pinned at the nape of her neck. Her sparkly grey-green eyes brightened her light brown face. Make no mistake, although she was kind, if there was something that rubbed her the wrong way, she would firmly let you know about it — a characteristic most would say about all of the Gaskin women. Grandmother Gaskin loved her family, church, and community. She worked with Aunt Harriet at the John Brown Home for the Aged, and she was also very involved in black women's organizations such as Syrings Court of Catanthe No. 25, Rizpah-Household of Ruth, 1161 of the Grand Order of Odd Fellows of Auburn, and Paul Noble Governors Movable Association of the Grand United Order of Odd Fellows of the Western Part of New York State. My grandmother and grandfather, along with other colored couples, also attended galas such as the Colored Ball and the Emancipation Ball.

I recall that my grandmother became very ill. She suffered for a long period with distention and stomach cancer. A surgical operation performed shortly before her death confirmed the fatal diagnosis. As she was nearing death during that late spring season, we were all gathered at the home of my grandparents at 77 Chapman. My grandfather, my parents, aunts, uncles, siblings, and cousins were assembled. The grownups and older children kept vigil at my grandmother's bedside. The drone of low voices filled the house; it seemed dark yet warm. I found myself playing alone under the kitchen table. Some days later, my grandmother spent her final hours at Mercy Hospital. I was almost four-years-old when Grandmother Gaskin passed away. She would be greeted at heaven's gate by all of those in the family that had gone before her—Aunt Harriet and her own daughters, Harriet, Ann, Mabel, Frances, Emma, and Rose. To be sure, it would be a glorious reunion. My grandfather was grief stricken. He had lost his better half. He made a public statement of thanks in the *Citizen Advertiser* to friends and family for their kindness and sympathy.

Years later, while compiling my research on the family, I learned that twenty years before my grandmother's death, she and her family attended the funeral of her famous aunt, Harriet Tubman Davis. Attending with her was her husband, Phillip Sr., and their children Richard, Jeanette, Rose, Phillip, and Alida. The youngest, Alida, also known to many as Lyda, was eight-years-old at the time. (She would become my mother.) Harriet Gaskin Waire and Mary Gaskin Walker—the eldest daughters—and their families lived in the New York City area and were not able to travel to Aunt Harriet's funeral. Sadly, the other Gaskin daughters, Ann, Mabel, Frances, and Emma, had all died of various lung conditions before the age of nineteen. Frances (two-years-old), Emma (eight-years-old), and Mabel (eighteen-years-old) died within two months of each other in the summer of 1905. Another child named Ann died shortly after birth.

Part Two

—

FAITH

CHAPTER FIVE

—

Home Going

One of the grand dames of Auburn, New York, was now dead. In many respects, as a grand dame, Harriet Tubman was an aberration. During her time, she did not possess the typical trappings of a lady of prestige, but she was a grand dame nonetheless. She was not wealthy, except in spirit. She was not ostentatious, except in her expectation, as a sympathizer, to provide freedom, food, clothing, and shelter for refugee slaves. It never ceased to amaze the historian, academician, or the common man or woman, as to the courage of this lady who risked life and limb to deliver slaves through the Underground Railroad across the Suspension Bridge over the Niagara Gorge to freedom in Canada. Notoriety and a distinct sense of reverence embraced her adult life. Her good friend Frederick Douglass said it best when he proclaimed Harriet Tubman to be the bravest of all abolitionists because she was willing to give her life for the cause in a way that few did.

The chestnut-colored woman's now ashen face and bony, chapped hands showed her ninety-plus years. Aunt Harriet Tubman Davis was peacefully nestled in a sick bed in the Home for the Aged, the place that she founded to provide tender healthcare and shelter for needy blacks. The whiteness of her crinkly hair melded into the soft white bed linens upon which she was laid. Her frail body assumed a comfortable posture, as if she was simply asleep. In life, she was grand, yet humble. She was strong, but gentle. She was self assured, however, accepted the help and generosity of others in the fight to abolish slavery. In death, her small frame betrayed the likelihood that she could personally rescue hundreds of men, women, and children from the jaws of slavery.

The Moses of Her People had indeed prepared for this day. Knowing that her end days were near, Harriet Tubman Davis made all of the arrangements for her own funeral. She told anyone who would listen that she had made peace with her impending death and that she was going home to make a place for those who she left behind. She was joyous in the anticipation of meeting the maker. In the days leading up to death, she could be heard singing. After a long battle with chronic bronchitis, Aunt Harriet went courageously to the other side with her chaplain, relatives, and close friends keeping vigil at her bedside. Nurse Ridgeway gently closed Harriet's eyelids and parched lips and folded her gnarled hands across the breast.

Most Auburnians knew that the brick house that majestically stood among many apple and pear trees and vegetable gardens on the Auburn–Fleming line was the place that Harriet Tubman Davis called home. For more than half a century, she created a safe haven there for herself, a second husband, family members, and other boarders. It was not a lavish life, but she worked hard and provided for the indigent. The homeless, the sick, and the aged found welcoming arms, a place to rest their heads, and food to suppress the gnawing hunger through challenging times. Often with little to spare, the grand dame made certain that there was enough for all to share from the cupboard and the cast iron pot that simmered on her wood-burning stove. When she returned from the Civil War and her numerous journeys to rescue freedom seekers in the South, she made her way down South Street Road to the place she called home—the familiar house on seven acres of land that had been purchased from Secretary of State William H. Seward. A former slave woman could not have asked for more. Harriet often confessed that her fondest wish was to die at home, but this was an unfulfilled dream.

On the evening of March 10, 1913, the news about the famed abolitionist's death surged throughout the nation. Telegraphs and telephone wires carried the message well beyond the hometown of General Tubman. While the white and black communities alike reluctantly accepted the truth, Harriet's personal nurse and the staff at the John Brown Home for the Aged prepared her body to be taken by the undertaker.

Harriet Tubman Davis had long since deeded the Home for the Aged and the 25 acres of land on which it stood to the A.M.E Zion Church. As she entered her elder years, the day-to-day operations of the home were managed by the board of trustees and the board of women managers. The funeral arrangements were carried out according to her wishes and were organized by family, friends, and clergy from the church, including Reverend A. Smith and Reverend E. U. A. Brooks. At 11:00 a.m. on March 13, 1913, family, close friends, and staff members gathered privately at the Home for the Aged to pay a final tribute to the home's founding mother. A 3:00 p.m. public service was held at the A.M.E Zion Church on Parker Street. Harriet's death came as no surprise to her family, as she had suffered greatly over the past year, and although Aunt Harriet was no longer of this life, she would always remain with them in spirit. The comfort of her faith, determination, independence, and compassion would now be a heart-felt memory. She had impacted each and every one of their lives in a special way.

The family attended both services and was awestruck by the magnitude of outpouring affection for their loved one. The short, dark-skinned woman, who in her early years had the strength of two men and who rescued hundreds of slaves seeking freedom in the North, was gone. My family no longer had the security of knowing that Aunt Harriet was just down the road a piece on South Street. Now, they could only call upon their bittersweet memories. Each one had known her personally. Each one had stories to tell. Each one was related by blood and lineage through one of Harriet's brothers or sisters.

The founder of the Home for The Aged had no children of her own. She and her husband Nelson, however, did unofficially adopt a daughter. The love that Harriet would have given to biological children was given freely to her "adopted" daughter, Gertie, and to the children of her siblings and their children. She held a special place for each one of them in her heart. She was not a woman who had to meet a certain criteria for family to be a big part of her life. Her compassion knew no limits, and family, in particular, was extremely important to her. Harriet embodied the family's time-tested value of taking care of one another. Whether it was food, clothing, or shelter, she always felt she had a God-given mandate to do what he wanted her to do. She saw it as a gift to take care of others. In some way, surviving family knew that she was leaving them with the same legacy.

Many nieces, nephews, grandnieces, and grandnephews survived Harriet. Most of them were in their middle years with families of their own. They were mindful that their aunt Harriet's life was a testament to and an example of godliness and selflessness. She once said that she was to take care of her people as God wanted her to do, not just for one day or for one week, but for as long as she lived.

Harriet's family and friends had witnessed a life of good works. It would be up to them now to step into her shoes. Most of them vowed to do their best, although some fell short of this promise. Real life and the complexities of it demanded a strong faith, determination, independence, and compassion. The family often let things like color, education, and occupation separate rather than unite them. This was not what Aunt Harriet would've wanted. Her death prompted relatives to reflect upon their lives and to think about whether they had learned the lessons she taught.

For the time being, they would celebrate the life of the Moses of Her People. Distinguished clergy from Syracuse, Binghamton, Ithaca, Rochester, and Auburn attended the funeral services to memorialize her. Regular church folks made their way to Parker Street in droves. Each person made his or her way to the casket. The great Conductor of the Underground Railroad was dressed in black. She appeared much smaller than she was in life. Her hands were folded beneath her breast and cradled a wooden cross. Years earlier, Queen Victoria queen of England bestowed upon Harriet a medal for her heroic deeds. It was notably pinned to her dress below her left shoulder. On this bitter cold March afternoon, everyone joined together to tribute a former slave woman whose death represented the end of the abolitionist era. As the crowd processed from the church, the choir's rendition of "Arise My Soul" filled the chamber. Harriet would have been pleased.

The chill in the air went right though her bones. Mary Gaskin and her daughter Alida marched with the others slowly and stoically around the bend toward the massive opening in the ground on the knoll. The casket was already positioned next to its final resting place. In the coffin laid the remains of Mary's grandaunt Harriet. Her husband, Phillip, and the older children, Richie, Jenny, Rose, and Phil, trailed behind the twosome. It seemed as if the entire town was there. They were all assembled to send the grand dame home. Clutching the hand of little Lyda, Mary and her family followed the crowd as it meandered through the West Lawn section in Fort Hill Cemetery. Each person found a place to stand. Once everyone was positioned, the throng created a human ring around the gravesite. The Gaskin family politely nudged their way forward and settled in among other relatives, Aunt Harriet's closest friends, visiting clergy, and regional dignitaries who comprised the inner circle. Whites and blacks came from far and wide to say their final goodbyes. Tears and memories trumped race that day. Harriet Tubman, their friend and relative, was dead.

The gray skies grew darker. The crisp air was pierced by the sound of a hearty baritone voice. Those familiar and final words burst forth: "Friends, we are gathered here today to send our sister Harriet home to her maker. We give our condolences to her family and friends and those who simply knew her as Aunt Harriet. She was kind, compassionate, and selfless, but of course, most would admit she was mighty feisty, too." Laughter rose from the crowd and momentarily lifted the solemn mood.

Those who knew Harriet knew her as a person determined to do what she felt was necessary, especially if it involved helping her people. She did not stand for a whole lot of nonsense, but at the same time, love emanated from every pore. Her tenacity and solid faith in God would be missed. Everyone, from the escaped former slaves to the wealthiest families, would miss her wit and storytelling. Mary's daughter Rose, Harriet's great-grandniece, had a voice that rivaled the best from any church choir. The funeral services were not complete until Rose rang out her angelic rendition of "Get on Board Little Children," one of her famous great-grandaunt's favorite songs.

There was no one quite like Mrs. Tubman Davis, and the likes of her would not be seen again. The greatest heroine of the abolition era was no more. Mary was heartbroken. Her aunt Harriet was the closest thing she had to a mother; she loved her dearly. Mary choked back the tears that streamed down her light brown face. Since her early teen years, this courageous woman had consoled her, laughed with her, cooked with her, and shared with her life's triumphs, challenges, and deaths. Mary was mentally exhausted. Her grandaunt was gone. So much of Mary's life was tied to the great heroine.

Even though Mary was now an adult with her own husband and children, she still considered Harriet Tubman's house on South Street Road as her home. Thinking of her young life there and other frequent visits to the seven-acre property was full of fond memories. The strong women of the house stood out the most in her mind. There was Aunt Harriet and her mother, Nana Rit. Each had her own unique brand of strength.

Each woman had her own way of nurturing all who sought the comforts of home and mothering inside the walls of the brick house on South Street Road.

Thoughts about death and her own mortality began to race through Mary's mind: "Young, old, sick, or fit as a fiddle, the Lord gives and the Lord takes away. No matter how much we love someone death steals them from us. We must all go through it one way or another, and our loved ones will do the same at our passing. Life is precious, yet very short. We only appreciate the meaningfulness of that when the people we love suddenly depart from this life."

In an instant, a vision of Mary's mother flashed before her. Everyone always said that Ann Marie Elliott was beautiful—black, wavy hair that fell below her shoulders and a smile that shone brightly against her creamy skin tone. Mary's memory lingered on the vision of her mother dressed in that beautiful white gown she wore for the colored emancipation ball. All blacks that could afford it looked forward to the affair. The women and men were dressed in their finest, and they celebrated, in solidarity, their freedom in the North. In the free North, they could gather in groups greater than five. Ann Marie was clearly one of the most beautiful women in attendance. The ogling and whispers, at times, made her feel self-conscious. Mary laughed to herself thinking about how her father used to tease her mother about her pretty hair. Mary remembered her mother playfully hitting at him, as she scurried away and escaped to another room.

The funeral services were over. Mary and her family made their way home. They traveled that familiar route from Fort Hill Cemetery to 69½ Chapman Avenue. It had been an extremely long day. When the family arrived at the homestead, it was dusk. Phillip Sr., Rose, Phillip, Jr., and Alida retired fairly quickly. Mary was restless and went into the kitchen to warm herself near the wood stove. She sat there for hours as bittersweet memories flooded her mind.

The burial of Harriet Ross Tubman Davis on March 13, 1913, Fort Hill Cemetery. Members of the Elliott Gaskin Stokes family were in attendance. Alida Gaskin (standing behind the coffin) was eight-years-old (above); Harriet Tubman (center, with white shawl) at the John Brown Home for the Aged. Marietta (Mary) Elliott is pictured standing back row, first from left.

CHAPTER SIX

—

South Street Road

M ary had always known that she was born in her aunt Harriet's home. In fact, her parents lived there for a few years before she was born. They stayed with Aunt Harriet until her mother was nearly ready to give birth to Martha Jeanette. The young family then moved to their first house on Thornton Street in Auburn. The growing family enjoyed their frequent visits to Aunt Harriet's house. Mary remembered when she and her little sister Nettie ran after the chickens and geese in their aunt's backyard. The girls also loved to run through the meadows on the property that stretched as far as the eye could see. In season, apple and peach trees were plentiful. She allowed the sights, sounds, and smells of the past to wash over her. She remembered it all as if it had happened yesterday. She and her sister waited anxiously for spring and summer to arrive each year so they could play outside. She could almost feel the summer breeze brushing her cheeks.

Oh yes, the chickens. Mary and Nettie teased them so. The chickens would cluck at the top of their lungs ("Cluck! Cluck-cluck-cluck-cluck!!!"), and the girls would laugh and giggle at the top of theirs. The girls teased the poor little birds to exhaustion and dared their feathered friends to nip at their ankles. No sooner had the commotion started, than the girls heard the back door open and slam shut. Annoyed and making no bones about it, Aunt Harriet or Nana Rit or Mamma would run after them with a broomstick and yell, "Lebe dem chickins lone." Sniggling mischievously, the girls acted like they didn't have any idea what the fuss was all about. All of a sudden, they were no longer Mary and Nettie: "Marietta! Martha Jeanette! Git in dis hous!"

Mary loved that old place. She had many fond memories of visits there. Besides her Aunt Harriet, Nana Rit, and Grandpa Ben, Uncle Nelson loomed large in her mind. Uncle Nelson was a tall man with a sturdy build and was not much for words, but he always had a half-smoked cigar dangling from his full lips. The family told stories of how he was a Civil War veteran. He fought for the freedom of the slaves. They also heard him tell that he knew of Aunt Harriet when she served in the Civil War. He saw her there, but she was too busy nursing and scouting to notice the young man who admired her grit. Unbeknownst to her, Nelson had followed Harriet to Fleming and became one of her boarders. A short time later, they married in the basement of the Central Presbyterian Church in Auburn.

Then, of course, there was the excitement in the house when everyone knew that Mary's mother was coming close to birthing the baby. Although Ann Marie and Thomas had moved their growing family to Thornton Street, when the time came near for giving birth, Aunt Harriet and Nana Rit took care of Anne Marie's every need. The house was still for hours; not much talking going on. Even the men, Uncle Nelson and her daddy, sat quietly in the front room awaiting the new life. As Mary remembered it, the birth was not an easy one. Her mother seemed to be in so much pain. Mary and Nettie were excited and frightened at the same. They longed to hug their mother and assure her that everything would be all right. Nighttime fell upon the house. The men rekindled the logs in the wood stove and lit the kerosene lamps. The soft glow of the lamps and the warmth of the stove provided a sense of serenity and security.

The women were in a room upstairs. Rustling and scurrying of footsteps could be heard overhead. Loud screams pierced the silence below. Muffled grunts and groans gradually subsided. Then, as clear as a bell, a baby's cry rang out. The men nodded and agreed that the cries sounded like that of a healthy baby. Mary and Nettie just looked at each other in wonderment and clung to each other in surprise. They had a new baby. Everyone in the house seemed to release a sigh of relief. They had a new baby with a healthy cry.

Nanna Rit descended the stairs, and with a big smile on her face, she declared, "Thomus, you'se gots ya' a big baby boy." He leaped for joy and headed up the stairs to see his wife and newborn son. Nettie and Mary followed. They all stepped into the room to find Aunt Harriet making sure that the mother and new baby were comfortable. They could see that the baby was content as it suckled his mother's breast. Tiny fingers with almost invisible fingernails peeked out from beneath a small white covering. The little boy had a head of black curls. Ann Marie looked exhausted yet serene. She motioned for the girls to come closer. They gingerly eased over to her side.

Smiling at her little daughters, she said she hoped that they were happy to have a new brother and that his name was Anthony. The girls were ecstatic. They couldn't wait to hold and kiss him. Seeing that their mother required much needed rest, Thomas quickly dismissed the girls. He spent the rest of the evening watching over his wife and son. Mary, Nettie, and their mother took turns holding and rocking baby Anthony who had no trouble crying loud and often. Those were the good old days. Mary thought of all of them, including her younger brother, Anthony. Life was good then. She was too young to think of anything else but the good times.

It all came to an abrupt end when beautiful Ann Marie died. The household was shaken. Thomas, Mary, Nettie, and Anthony were devastated. It seemed as though nothing could console them. It was a sad state of affairs. The children were motherless, and their father no longer had the love and companionship of his wife.

The original residence of Harriet Tubman Davis is on the Auburn-Fleming line on South Street Road. The original house was wood. After a fire in the early 1880s, it was rebuilt with brick. The brick two-story structure was referred to as the family homestead. Harriet Tubman bought the house and seven acres of land from William H. Seward. At the time of printing the first edition of this book, the house was undergoing renovation and it is to be renamed the Harriet Tubman Museum. (circa 2008)

CHAPTER SEVEN

—

Finding Love

After their mother's death, their daddy was never the same. His gleaming smile rarely appeared across his full lips. He worked as much as he could when he could find work as a day laborer or whitewasher. It was no secret that his motivation to work had waned. A pervasive sadness consumed him. In his somberness, he felt so alone. Even though Mary, Martha, and Anthony were his pride and joy, he found it hard to express these feelings. They seemed lost to him now. Without saying a word, Martha and Mary knew what the other was thinking. They felt their father emotionally slipping away from them. His youthfulness was now substituted with a visible aging quality about him.

It seemed like yesterday that their father had a palpable zeal for life and freedom. He was known to be his own man, and he did not let too many folks, black or white, keep him from doing exactly what he wanted to do. Life itself could be a day-to-day struggle, but he accepted the struggle because he was no longer a slave. He was a free man, and the Negroes around him were also free. Many of the whites lived side-by-side with the coloreds; strong friendships and working relationships were forged. The working men of Auburn—laborers to chauffeurs to shop owners to company owners—depended on each other to keep the bustling local economy growing. Each, in his own way, carved out a gratifying life for himself and his family. Most were satisfied to be working no matter the occupation. Hard work was the clarion call of the day.

It was not uncommon for Negro men to own their own land and houses. The houses were either built or purchased from whites. Several men in the family located properties on Thornton Street, Chapman Avenue, and Union Avenue. Thomas was fortunate to purchase his property at 31 Union Avenue from Charles M. Cootes, a well-respected court judge in Auburn. He, his wife, and their daughters enjoyed the comforts of the well-to-do. Cootes owned several properties on Union Avenue, including his own well-appointed home at 29 Union Avenue. On the next lot, Thomas built a modest home for his wife, Ann Marie, and his children, Mary, Martha Jeanette, and Anthony. Life seemed so simple and predictable then. Hard work and family consumed every waking hour, until tragedy struck.

Not even the dangers of escaping slavery could compare to the trauma of losing his beautiful Ann Marie. He remembered her as a sweet, innocent young girl on the Brodess Plantation in Dorchester County, Maryland. She was the granddaughter of two people whom he truly admired. Even though he lived on the Pritchett Meredith Plantation, he, like other slaves in Dorchester, knew of the Rosses. Benjamin Ross was a God-fearing man, and he was the preacher at the Bazzel Church. Slaves flocked to his church every Sunday to hear him ignite their souls with the spirit of Jesus, to comfort their minds, and to inspire them to endure their earthly journey while continuing to crave justice and freedom. He never wavered from the conviction that God would provide for their every need in every way. The slaves not only trusted God; they trusted Ben. They also knew that much of his strength came from the love and undying support of his wife, Rit. There was something about the way that she carried herself. Her head was always held high. She was warm and welcoming, but no one, not even the whites, dared to cross her, especially when it came to her family. She would sooner die than let harm come to her husband and children. She never forgave the white master for selling her daughters Linah and Sophe into slavery farther south. She vowed that it would never happen again. Someone would pay.

Both Ben and Rit instilled their love of God, family, and freedom into their children, grandchildren, and the other slaves in Dorchester County. Thomas held dear to those values, and the idea of running away to the land of freedom in the North was never far from his thoughts. He was confident that if the Rosses' adult children, Harriet, Harry, Benjamin, Robert, Henry, and Moses, had escaped successfully, he could too. It was simply a matter of time. Ann Marie was also never far from his thoughts. He often daydreamed of her loveliness, and she would soon be of marriageable age. He desired to have her as his wife, and he made his intention known.

One Sunday morning, Thomas finally mustered up the nerve to approach Ben Ross after his sermon and fellowship with the church members. Thomas made his way to the reverend, thanked him for his God-inspired message, and asked to speak with him privately. Ben nodded yes and motioned Thomas to walk with him along the briar path away from the others. Thomas wasn't known for being down in the mouth, but at that moment, he felt very nervous and searched his mind for the right words. It felt as if he was babbling on and on, but he finally got the words out. He explained how much he admired the Rosses and how he was personally inspired by their faith in God, commitment to family, and quest for freedom. He talked about how he wanted to have these same things in his life, and he wanted to share them with Ann Marie. For the first time in a long while, Thomas felt like a small boy asking his father for the impossible.

Thomas' affection for Ben's granddaughter had not gone unnoticed. Both Ben and Rit had wondered when this day would come. Ben, however, did not acquiesce so quickly. Instead, he took the opportunity to make it clear to Thomas what kind of man he wanted for his granddaughter. He wanted a man who would look past her physical beauty. No one could deny her obvious attractiveness. Her creamy complexion, full lips, and below-the-shoulder wavy hair made both men and women look at her twice. The softness of her cheeks and her pouty lips only enhanced the countenance of her face. Ben went on to say that her husband must honor her womanhood. He must provide for her and protect her. He would not burden her with unnecessary hardships for slavery was hard enough. There would be no womanizing, excessive drinking, or physical violence. God willing that children be born, they too should be provided for and protected. There was no greater commitment a man could make than to feed, clothe, and establish a home for his family. This was his God-given duty.

Thomas was further admonished that a husband should save every penny, understanding that Negro men often had to purchase their wives' freedom and where possible, buy the freedom of their children or other relatives. It may be a long time in coming, but freedom was to be strived for, and he should never forget the importance of taking care of each other. Finally, Ben declared that trust in God was not negotiable. It was as essential as the breath of life. No man, woman, or child could live honorably without the word of God. Thomas had not expected to hear a sermon for his ears only, but felt even closer to Ben as a result of it. Ben asked Thomas if he could commit to these values. Picturing Ann Marie in his mind's eye and feeling his great love for her, Thomas assured Ben that he would be the kind of man and husband that Ann Marie needed and deserved. With his arms held open, Ben embraced the young Thomas. Although he was grateful and satisfied, a tearful Ben knew that Thomas could not fully apprehend that he was just beginning a lifetime of hard work, challenges, triumphs, and personal losses. Ben gave Thomas his blessings and assured him that God would be with him.

CHAPTER EIGHT

—

The Great Escape

D eath. Mary felt as though death was determined to follow her. Yes, death was a part of life, but it was so painful. It was the kind of thing that took your breath away. Each time it happened, that empty feeling seemed to last forever. The losses seemed too much for her to bear. Aunt Harriet, Nanna Rit, Grandpa Ben, Mamma, Anthony, Daddy, and Martha Jeanette's daughter Gertrude Lee were all gone. Then there was Uncle Nelson and her angels Ann, Frances, Emma, and Mabel who had all departed from this life. Mary was left with nothing but a place in her heart where she would cherish them. Life had to go on. One did not have much choice in the matter, yet every time things seemed to get back to normal, death raised its ugly head again and snatched the life of someone she held dear. Searching her soul and looking for God to reveal the answer to death, Mary was left with just bittersweet memories of those she loved. They had passed from this life to the next. All had transitioned to the spiritual world, never to be touched or loved in the same way again. She would keep their memories alive by holding them in that special place in her heart. Heaviness settled into her chest. She collected herself. She could not allow herself to sink into the depths of depression and self-pity. Childhood diseases and adult maladies and natural causes had to be accepted. There was one loss, though, that she would never understand. The death of her father, Thomas Elliott, would always remain a mystery.

Mary moved closer to the wood stove. The past few days had been exhausting. Aunt Harriet's death was a tremendous loss, not only for the family, but for the entire community as well. Mary poked the logs in the stove hoping that the fire would yield enough warmth to sit a little longer in her kitchen at 69½ Chapman. Her father's face lingered in her mind. He had been dead now almost twenty years, but his smooth, dark brown skin and gleaming smile made her spirit merry for the moment. She nestled into her chair and remembered him.

Aunt Harriet and the other elders were so proud of her father. Mary always knew that the elders had a deep respect for her dad. Thomas was born on the Eastern Shore of Maryland, and raised on the Meredith Plantation, in the same vicinity where Aunt Harriet and her family lived. Mary always knew that her father was known to be a strong and courageous man. In fact, he was one of the renowned Dover Eight. She remembered the story that was told over and over and over again about her father's escape from slavery. Mary and her little sister, Martha Jeanette, could recite the story as if they had been there. Mary recalled one evening at her aunt Harriet's house. All of the folks who were staying with Aunt Harriet at the time and the Elliotts were gathered in the backyard. And as usual, her aunt Harriet had captured everyone's attention. Motioning for the family to move in closer, Aunt Harriet said, "Lets me tells ya' bout Thomus an' de Dova' Eight."

Aunt Harriet was a great storyteller. She captured the spirit of the story, hand gestures and all, and conveyed it in such a way that you could imagine you were there. Mary, Martha Jeannette, and the others clung to her every word. They knew they were in for a good story. They had their fill of vegetable stew and corn bread and gathered together in the yard to listen to (and relive) the great escape. Aunt Harriet's voice resonated, as she began telling Thomas' story with great pride:

"I hears from abolishunists and thru da' grapevine 'bout what happen down dere cuz I wuz in Canada at da time. I ben there for a numba of years. Dey says that my daddy in big trouba' cuz he trys to hep da runaways. The law was agin' him and dey wants to put my daddy in jail. My daddy hides Thomus and da'othas in Car'line Coun'ie da nite dey escapes. Ya' knows it wus agin' the law for folks, white or black, to hep runaways. Law or no law, my daddy was gonna hep any black body he could. Thomus, yo' daddy here, and da' othas 'scape from dey mastahs. Thomus wuz from da Mer'dith Plantation. Da othas from oder plantations nearsby. Dere was fibe mens an' two womans. All eight of dem 'cided it wus time to goes. Time to 'scape slav'ry. Dey was givin' the way to goes by da good friends of da Unda' Groun' Railroad. It wusn't easy. Dey 'scapes and da' white ownas wus gonna pays $3,000 fo' da slabes to be brung back to dem."

Harriet continued to captivate her audience, and she recounted the rest of the story. The fugitives made it safely all the way to Camden, Delaware. They managed to evade the patrollers stationed at many locations along the road. It was later understood that the group of eight had confided in a black man who betrayed them. They say the man's name was Thomas Otwell. Otwell told the runaways that he would take them to the house of Harriet's good friend William Brinkley. Otwell mentioned Harriet Tubman and her work on the

Underground Railroad, and he gained their confidence by saying that that he had been to the house with her many times before. He wanted a share of the $3,000 reward so bad that he could taste it. Otwell revealed the whereabouts of the slaves to the Dover sheriff. (To this day, people of African descent refer to other blacks that engage in this type of behavior as Uncle Toms.)

The sheriff and his men set out to round up and arrest the runaways. They knew exactly where to find them—hiding in a wooded area not far from Dover. The white men armed with guns quietly came up behind them. Each white man pointed his weapon at the head of a slave. The sheriff made it abundantly clear that they would die right then and there if they did not get down on their knees. With great satisfaction in his voice, the sheriff rancorously said, "Dead niggas tell no tales."

Thomas and the others were horrified. They were not far from their destination when they were captured. They believed that Otwell had ruined their chances at gaining freedom. The slaves were roughened up, bound, and taken to the Dover jail. The small jail was overcrowded with vagrants and other miscreants, so the sheriff decided to detain the slaves in an area over the jail. Thomas and the other men had to find a way to get out of there. They devised a way for two of the men to begin untying the ropes that bound the hands of the others. They knew this had to be done swiftly. Sweat poured down their dark faces, but they were confident that they could escape. The men conferred as to how they could manage the escape. They decided to take hot coals from the stove and start a fire. Within minutes, the fire was blazing and the smoke and heat filled the room. Two of the men broke the window, and one-by-one they jumped down twelve feet to the ground level below. By the grace of God, none were injured. There was only one way to escape—over the stone wall.

Without hesitation, the fugitives helped each other over it. By then, the sheriff found the upper loft ablaze. Furious, he ran down to the area behind the jail with his rifle pointed at their backsides. The last backside went over the wall when he tried to blast several rounds, but the gun misfired. He and his men rallied and ran after the slaves, but it was no use. The slaves were long gone. Newspapers in towns for miles around carried the story about the great escape.

Without being captured, the Dover Eight found their way back to Camden where they were secreted by William Brinkley and other agents on the road. About two weeks later, Brinkley and friends took the fugitives by wagon through Dover and Smyrna—the worst places on the Underground Railroad. Harriet's friend Thomas Garrett from Wilmington, Delaware, also assisted the Dover Eight. Agents of the underground route guided them through to Chester County, Philadelphia. Once there, William Still and members of the Vigilance Committee received them warmly. Still was the head of the Vigilance Committee and recorded the tale of the Dover Eight, as told by Thomas Elliott, Gerard Hughes, and other agents in the abolitionist movement.

The Dover Eight episode prompted Harriet to go south to Dorchester County, Maryland, to free her parents. She was concerned that the authorities were going to put her father in jail, because they knew that Ben Ross had harbored the Dover Eight during their escape.

Harriet continued telling the story to family gathered at her home in Fleming: "I goes down dere. Thomus an' dem already gon'. Momma and Daddy dere whens I cum. Good, Lawd Almighty, my good frens heps me. I takes Momma and Daddy alls da ways to Kanada to da Promiz Lan'. We gets dere in Kanada. Da wetha' wuz not good. Momma and Daddy, dey ole' bones cundnt' take it. My fren', Willyim Suwod, sells me dis here hous' in Flemin', Nue Yark. He a good man. I brings Mamma and Daddy here. An' here we is. Rain, sun, or snow, da' wetha' bedder fo' dem here, den da' wetha' furtha' no'th. Dey likes it here. An' I likes havin' dem here wif me in Flemin'. Ain't nuffin like havin' fam'ly 'round ya'."

Mary and Nettie knew they belonged to a special family. They grew accustomed to seeing all kinds of folks around. There was a parade of people, other than family, who resided with their aunt Harriet for days, weeks, or longer. She recalled that her aunt Harriet opened her home to anyone in need, especially colored folks who had fallen on hard times or needed a safe place to stay on their way to Canada or who wanted to start a new life in Auburn. She did not have much, but what she did have was there to share with black folks in need. The Moses of Her People carried a goodness and compassion in her heart until her death. Mary and her family knew of Aunt Harriet's love and caring all too well.

CHAPTER NINE

—

Hard Times

A lthough known for his great slave escape, Thomas Elliott was now a broken man. Once strong and courageous, he was shaken to the core by the death of his beloved. His faith was irrevocably destroyed. Why had God taken her from him? She was his greatest joy. Coming home to her each night made it all worth it. Her gentleness, her warmth, and her quiet strength evaporated in death. His heart ached for fear that he could never recapture their love and intimacy. Ann Marie knew him better than any other living soul. He sobbed loudly and uncontrollably, but he found no comfort and sincere condolences only nauseated him. With each successive moment, a bitter loneliness swelled within him. How could God do this to him and his children? He searched his soul for answers.

Was it because on occasion he secretly lusted for some young, sweet thing? He never did anything about it. Was it because he lusted for Ann Marie halfway through the workday? Maybe he didn't work hard enough, or maybe he had not given his children enough. What had he done wrong? Why had God Almighty punished him so mercilessly? He thought of his wife's late grandfather Ben. Had he broken the promises that he made Ben to provide for and protect his granddaughter? Thomas was certain that he had done everything in his power to take care of her, but it was clear to him that his love and commitment were not enough. In his wisdom, God left him without the affection and companionship of his wife and left his children motherless. What kind of God would do that?

Mary and Martha Jeanette witnessed their father's grief. The girls tried to help little Anthony keep the memory of his mother alive; their father rarely mentioned their mother. All they knew was that their father was not a happy man. He was quiet to a fault. When he came home from work in a mood, they knew not to bother him. The girls made sure he had enough to eat, but all the children had to do was look into his eyes to know that he had no tolerance for noise or chatter. He would bide his time in the kitchen, sitting at the table near the wood stove and staring aimlessly into the distance. Who knew what was on his mind. But the children knew well enough to leave him with his thoughts. Engaging their father in conversation about the activities of the day grew less and less. Silent evenings grew into silent mornings. Happiness, the unmistakable chatter of children, and the robustness of a growing family had died with Ann Marie. Perhaps Thomas' single transgression was not letting the world know how much he loved her. The children learned to accept their father's irreversible change in personality.

Little Anthony tried to be as helpful as he could, and he did not complain as he went about doing his chores. His sisters had taught him how to collect fresh eggs and to keep the chicken coop clean. It was also his job to take the kitchen scraps and put them in the compost pile. He also carried firewood from the back shed to restock the woodpile for the stove. He never tired of hearing his sisters compliment him on what a good job he had done. Physically, Anthony was strong for his age, but he did become ill more than what was usual. Everything would be just fine, and without notice, he would awake with high fever, pain throughout his small frame, fatigue, and bouts of severe coughing. His sisters did the best they could to keep him comfortable, using herbs and teas to relieve his symptoms.

The vigil often took several days. They worried so about their brother's health. No doctor in the area took on black patients. With the help of the older women nearby, Mary and Nettie would nurse him back to health. Childhood diseases were all too common. Some, in fact, were fatal. Families across the community and around the country, black and white, feared for the lives of their young, who often fell victim to tuberculosis, whooping cough, cholera, small pox, or yellow fever. Infant deaths, childhood mortality, and childhood morbidity were a constant reminder of what was an unpleasant, but often expected, part of life.

Thomas realized that the family needed a woman's touch in the household. He pulled himself together enough to find another woman who could be a wife, mother, and nursemaid for him and his children. Helen was a good woman. She and Thomas were not married in the traditional sense, but she went about her day fashioning a stable home at 31 Union Avenue. She realized full well that she was in the house of Thomas' deceased wife, but she tried her best to create a stable home life for Thomas and his children. The children prayed that the new woman of the house would bring their father out of his somberness, but deep down they knew that she could never replace their mother.

They called her Miss Helen. She was a very good cook, so Mary and Nettie learned everything there was to learn about cooking. Their favorite: chicken stew and biscuits. There was always a pot of something savory on the stove. Miss Helen also showed them how to launder and iron clothes and how to clean the house properly. She also took care to keep Anthony busy; he was full of energy and a bit mischievous. It was not always easy to share space with a new woman in the house, but they all made the best of it. Thomas did not seem to care about the mechanics of homemaking or relationship building. He made himself scarce most of the time. When he was around, he was a cantankerous old soul.

Ann Marie Ross Stewart, niece of Harriet Tubman (above); Thomas Elliott, one of The Dover Eight, married Ann Marie Ross Stewart. They are the author's great-grandparents.

CHAPTER TEN

—

Crossing Over

H elen had lived with Thomas and the children for a short
while, when Anthony grew ill again. This time, it was
the worst they had ever seen him. The coughing, chills, and
fever just would not let up. Thomas and the girls called upon
Aunt Harriet to come and assess the situation. She set out from
her home in Fleming, walked down South Street Road toward
Auburn, and made her way to 31 Union Avenue.

Harriet had been taught by the best. Her parents, Rit and
Ben, knew every herb, poultice, and tea to be used in sick
cases. The freedom fighter as a young sickly child herself often
needed her parents' knowledge and skill. The most memorable
time was when she suffered a severe head wound at the hands
of her overseer. Her parents could alleviate many ailments and
sicknesses, and they passed that information down to Harriet.
As General Tubman, she was known to use their remedies to
help the soldiers during the Civil War.

When Harriet Tubman Davis arrived, she moved swiftly to
Anthony's bedside. Looking at the boy's drawn face, she sat
herself alongside him on the bed. She carefully opened his
eyelids and checked his pupils and the whites of his eyes for
discoloration. She turned the damp cloth on his forehead to

the cooler side and placed it gently above his brows. She called for more water to freshen the cloth. She immediately knew that her nephew was not doing well at all. She stayed with the family for several days, but she knew that nothing in her arsenal of medicinal plants and herbs would break the deadly hold the disease had on the boy. The entire household braced for the worst. Everyone except for Thomas prayed for Anthony's return to health. Thomas saw no value in asking for the impossible.

With each passing hour, the boy seemed to slip further and further away. The women folk grew cautiously optimistic when they heard him occasionally mumble in delirium. Thomas went into the room infrequently. He stood in the door for a minute or two and returned to the kitchen table or sat outdoors alongside the house. He did not share his thoughts or feelings with anyone. It was if he knew that the inevitable was going to happen. Death knocked at the door of 31 Union again. Thomas' only son had died.

Thomas' reaction was very unusual for he did not shed a tear. It was as if this was a daily occurrence. Perhaps it was his way of shielding himself from the pain of death. Mary and Martha were inconsolable. Their little brother had not yet reached ten years of age. His life was not spared. Aunt Harriet and Helen tried desperately to comfort them. The house was filled with the female cries and wails of mourning. As evening drew near, the silence in the house was overwhelming. Together Harriet and Helen prepared the home for friends and family to view the body of Anthony Elliott and to pay their final respects in his father's house.

After the wake and funeral services, Thomas disappeared for several days. This was not the first time. Helen and the girls worried that he would not return, but he always did. There was never any mention of where he spent his time away from home. Helen was not naive, but she could not and would not confront Thomas. The last thing she wanted to do was upset him. For several months, any talk that he perceived to be critical or judgmental pushed him into a maniacal tirade. His ranting and raving were frightening. Helen and the girls cowered and sat frozen with fear, praying that he would not physically harm them. During these episodes, his rants were unintelligible. Once he began to calm down, he would complain of severe headache pain. This could go on for hours. Sometimes the headache pain was so severe that it was followed by a general weakness or numbness in his arms and legs. He began to work less and less.

The people in town began to whisper about Thomas. They had heard for years about his courageous escape from slavery as one of the renowned Dover Eight. He was well-liked and was considered to be a trustworthy, hardworking family man, but he had changed so much after his wife died that his family received very few visitors at the house anymore. Thomas found it more difficult to find work as a laborer, whitewasher, or coachman. He enjoyed his work, but few establishments or private homeowners were willing to pay for his services. The word had spread that Thomas was out of control and was not thinking clearly. Without warning, he became emotional and erratic—anything could set him off.

By and by Thomas found himself taking that long haul from his house down to South Street and from South Street to the old wooden rookery on North Street near the bridge. The long trek seemed to calm him. Along the way, he would think about his early days in Canada as a newly freed slave. He marveled at the sight of free Negroes living in houses rather than shacks and at how black folks worked and made a daily wage. He had truly reached the Promised Land. A few years later, he heard of opportunities for work in Auburn, New York. He was willing to take on a new adventure. It was there in that small town that he married the love of his life, pretty girl Ann Marie. Until they could purchase property of their own, they lived with Ann Marie's aunt Harriet Tubman. Everyone, including Thomas, called her Aunt Harriet. Their oldest daughter, Mary, was born in Aunt Harriet's home on South Street Road. The Elliott family always referred to the frame house on the Auburn-Fleming line as their first home. Mary, Nettie, and baby Anthony enjoyed their visits to the seven-acre property. While living with his wife's aunt Harriet Tubman, he remembered spending time with Nelson, Harriet's second husband, and Ben, Harriet's father. The three of them would gather there after a hard day's work. Nelson, chewing on his cigar, talked about his Civil War days; Ben preached a little here and there, but mostly talked about how God had led him and his family to freedom. They were both gone now. Rit, Harriet's mother, had also passed. His beloved Ann Marie and their young son, Anthony, had crossed over, too. The configuration of the family had changed so drastically over the past ten years. Letting these bittersweet memories evaporate into the evening air, Thomas ascended the back stairwell to the second floor of the old wooden rookery.

The women who lived on the second floor of the old wooden rookery were thought to be ladies of the evening. They welcomed men and allowed them to enter into a world of passion and compassion. There the men found the essence of femininity. Softness, openness, and giddy laughter made all cares disappear for an evening. The passionate and sexual appetite of a waiting man was satisfied completely. Man was made one with woman. Thomas had resisted being drawn to the ladies, but he could no longer push back his need for sexual intimacy. He didn't want the gentle caresses and the loving closeness he had shared with his beloved. Instead, he craved the free and wild conquest of the ladies of the evening. They anticipated his visits. After several encounters, Thomas started to request the company of one particular yellow girl. The yellow girl was strikingly beautiful and, in so many ways, she reminded him of Ann Marie.

He found himself longing to be with her. He sought to spend as much time with the yellow girl as possible. The only thing that he neglected to realize was that this beautiful lady had captured the heart and minds of many men. She soothed them, satiated them, and left them begging for more. Thomas was obsessed and confused. He realized that he was falling in love with a woman who shared herself with other men. The woman could not abide by Thomas' ferocious jealousy and would no longer see him. She would not belong to any one man. No matter how many times he showed up at the rookery, he was abruptly turned away. Confused and belligerent, Thomas could not let go. On a hot and humid summer evening, he returned to the rookery with a pistol, and he began shooting sporadically into the air and at the second-floor rooms. He demanded attention. He wanted the world to know that he would not leave without spending time with the woman who had captured his heart. He had enough ammunition to load and reload again. The firings were loud and consistent. People on the second floor of the rookery scampered to stay low away from the windows. Thomas positioned himself on the ground below, as if he was guarding the Taj Mahal. No one except for him would be intimate with the yellow girl ever again.

Thomas was arrested. He was charged with attacking a woman with a pistol. A grand jury was impaneled, and Judge Charles M. Cootes presided. The jury returned the verdict that there was no evidence that Thomas Elliott deliberately attempted to harm the woman in question. But it did not end there. A short time later, Judge Cootes retired and Judge Day assumed responsibility for the case. Under Judge Day, three doctors proclaimed that the defendant Thomas Elliott was in fact insane, and the criminal case quickly became a matter of mental health. After a robust examination of Thomas' life and recent behavior, the medical authorities deemed the former freedom seeker a lunatic. His loss of memory, intense headaches, poor judgment, unintelligible rants, and erratic behavior supported the diagnosis. Within six months, it was adjudicated that Thomas Elliott be remanded to the Utica Asylum.

Helen and the girls were devastated. They had witnessed the changes in Thomas, but that did not affect their love for him. In fact, they tried even harder to make him comfortable and happy. They heard the gossip and whispers about him, but it never crossed their minds that he would be labeled as insane. The entire town knew about the shooting at the rookery. What was he thinking? That was the problem—he wasn't. But was he a lunatic? The family tried to make sense of all that had happened. Insanity. Lunacy. Neither made any sense. It was a frightening state of affairs. Thomas would be put away for the rest of his life, and the family would be subjected to public and familial ridicule. Most people believed that insanity ran in the family and that is was incurable. Although they were a proud family, Helen and the girls were afraid of being shunned. They soon realized that it was a very small world. What they had endured in private was now made public. But more importantly, they had to reconcile with the fact that Thomas would be lost to them forever.

Everyone heard nothing but horror stories about how patients were treated in asylums. Many inmates never returned to their families. Thomas Elliott, the courageous freedom seeker and escaped slave, would now be held captive in the mental institutional system of New York State. From slavery on a plantation to incarceration in a mental hospital, Thomas' mind, body, and spirit would again be confined in horrific conditions. Without any prescription for rehabilitation, treatment, or cure, the taste of freedom vanished the day four white men deemed Thomas as insane.

Helen carefully prepared a small satchel containing his shaving cup, soap and razor, a clean pair of overalls, a work shirt, wool socks, and a corncob pipe with a small bag of tobacco. She and the girls went to the courthouse to see Thomas off before he and several other men were transported to Utica Asylum. It was simply called Old Main, because of the historic and architectural design of the main building.

CHAPTER ELEVEN

—

Another World

Q uite confused, Thomas was hauled to the asylum with the
other patients. They were corralled into the back of a
wagon—driven by two coachmen and a team of Morgan
Horses—and were directed to sit on wooden benches nailed to
the floor. Each person was chained to the other to prevent
escape. The other men were white. All of them, including
Thomas, were unshaven, disheveled, and disoriented. The
stench in the enclosed wagon was putrid. This was the telltale
sign that this particular wagon had been used time and time
again to haul the likes of these men to what would become
their final residence. It was not likely that they would ever
return home again. Although they departed from Auburn,
several of the men transported to Old Main hailed from cities
and towns across New York State.

The dreaded classification of being labeled insane by the
most brilliant minds practicing psychiatry foreshadowed the
barbaric treatment that was in store for patients bearing this
diagnosis. Thomas sank into the bench. He stared at each one
of the other passengers. His eyes traveled across their faces,
down their bodies, and rested upon their shoes. The men
cowered in their seats, mumbled under their breath, and

squirmed in place. One man had a ferocious laugh. He was frightening. Another man continued to bang his head against the wagon walls. Another man stunk of feces and urine, but his smile (although accentuated by jagged, rotten teeth) was gleeful. A few others sat and stared aimlessly into space. One man was bound and laid doubled up in what amounted to be a small cage. Thomas found himself trying to release himself from the shackles. Hot tears streamed down his chestnut-colored cheeks. His entire life flashed before his eyes. He knew he wasn't dead, but he did not feel alive. The mumbling voices, other noises, and stench of the horse-drawn carriage was something he could not believe. Thomas searched his memory to try and piece together how he had ended up here. He saw rolling visions of Ann Marie and his children, Mary, Nettie, and Anthony. Helen, Harriet, and all of the others came to his mind, too. The images quickly faded. His head ached terribly as he tried to put it all together. Tears still flowing, he lurched forward trying to break the chains that enslaved him. What had brought him to this place? Fleeting thoughts took him back to the old wooden rookery. Just beyond the blurry veil shrouding his mind, he saw a woman running and screaming. He felt the butt of a pistol in his hand. The smell of sulfur and arid smoke filled his nostrils.

He wanted her, but she wanted nothing to do with him. Anger rose in his chest. He breathed heavily, and it felt as though his heart was trying to escape through his chest. What had he done? What terrible sin had he committed? Why was he sitting there with these men traveling to an unknown place? An overwhelming sense of helplessness overtook him. He cried out searching for answers. The pounding of horses' hooves clamoring against the earth drowned the answers out. He was now on the road to a place where his spirits would be further broken.

The coachmen approached the massive stone building with its colossal white columns. The human cargo was unloaded. They were hitched together with iron shackles, as if being delivered to a distant plantation for slave work. The men were led to check into their new residence. They were taken to a holding area that was separated from the patients who had already adapted to daily life at Old Main. Thomas possessed the wherewithal to know, at that moment, that he had escaped slavery once, but he knew that he could never escape the stone and iron confines that now engulfed him. Fear and hopelessness crept throughout his inner being. He let out an audible gasp, and shuddered into a stupor. From slavery to freedom to insanity, this is not how Thomas had predicted that he would spend his end years.

A white man in a white uniform took Thomas to a white shower room—everything was stark white. After washing with white soap, it became clear to Thomas that he despised the color white in every way that it manifested itself. No matter whether it was a person, a piece of clothing, the color of an endless hallway, or the bedcovers that encased him during treatments, Thomas Elliott had an undying desire to escape the whiteness of his surroundings. But there was no way out. He had to learn how to adapt and conform to his new life in order to survive.

Even during his healthy years, Thomas was not a conformist. In freedom, he relished his ability to hold his head high and walk about the streets of Auburn and St. Catharines without having to carry a pass or a note like a nervous schoolboy. He cherished the right to own land and a home. He held dear his ability to earn a wage to take care of his family. Now, he had no personal freedoms. He was incarcerated and subjected to a daily regime that stripped him of all dignity and respect of a free man.

After being scrubbed clean and dressed in hospital garb, he was taken to the infirmary for a physical exam. All the scars, lesions, and physical irregularities were noted. He was then taken through an annex and was seated in an office with a white man whose persona exuded clinical authority. The psychiatrist questioned Thomas as to his understanding of why he had been remanded to the Utica Asylum. The lengthy interview resulted in the doctor annotating the admissions records and leaving Thomas feeling that nothing he said could reverse his inevitable stay at Old Main.

No amount of medical treatment was known to penetrate the mind of an insane person, bringing back a healthy state, before he slipped into the confusion, detachment, fear, paranoia, and violence of mental illness. As asylums sprang up across the country, thousands of people were warehoused in institutions where they were relegated to isolation and confinement from their families and communities. Thomas was now one of them. Every inmate was expected to earn his keep by working in the gardens, wood shops, kitchens, cleaning squads, and on other maintenance work teams to upkeep Old Main. There were some inmates like Thomas who were unable to work due to the progressive nature of the disease. Prevalent therapies such as ice baths, electroshock, and confinement to adult-sized cribs or cages were used to tranquilize the more irascible patients. These patients were essentially locked away in the worst wards. They were dark, damp, and filthy with little to no light. The fainthearted were hard pressed to work there.

The most severe cases were housed in these designated areas within the facility. Thomas was diagnosed as a severe case. His physical health and mental acuity deteriorated rapidly once he was admitted. His condition worsened to the extent that he was paralytic. But he endured a fate much worse than death at Old Main. After two years of incarceration, Thomas was merely a shell of the disturbed man who had entered Utica Asylum. He was emaciated, paralyzed, and filthy with matted, kinky hair. His once youthful face had aged well beyond his forty-six years. He was all but dead.

The Utica Asylum was overcrowded and needed room for an increasing population of mentally ill patients. Thomas Elliott was discharged and admitted to the Willard Asylum in Ovid, New York. Poor Thomas was so lethargic that he did not comprehend his trek—first by carriage and then by boat—to the esteemed Willard. Its prestigious architectural details, pastoral setting, and grand acreage eluded him. In his coma-like state he was oblivious to the spectacular foliage that was bursting with magnificent colors—sunrise yellow, pumpkin orange, and vivid red.

At Willard, an institution made infamous for its treatment of the mentally ill, Thomas took his last breath two weeks after admission. His lifeless body was interred unceremoniously. His coffin was crudely crafted by men at Willard who were assigned this task to insure nominal burial costs for the facility. His gravesite is located on the knoll to the left of the elm tree, beyond the sections where the Jews and men who served in the military were buried. Thomas was buried, as was customary, a day after he died. Helen, Mary, and Martha were notified after Thomas was buried. Thomas Elliott lay lifeless in the Willard Cemetery. No one thought it necessary to inform the family that Thomas' mind and body had been ravaged by general paresis of the insane, which was caused by syphilis, an untreatable disease at the time. In lieu of a headstone, Thomas' grave was marked with a metal disk engraved with his own personal number rather than his name. Thomas was buried in the eighty-seventh lot in the fifth row. He was the 568th person to be buried at Willard Cemetery. His was a life lost too early.

One hundred and twenty-five years after his death, descendants of Thomas Elliott located his burial site in Willard Cemetery. My daughters Michele and Adrianne and myself, Joyce Stokes Jones, arranged for a proper memorial service. On October 9, 2010, family and thirty others gathered around a newly placed gravestone to memorialize Thomas Elliott. We celebrated all of what was his life, underscoring his renowned escape from slavery, and his fight for freedom. On a beautiful autumn day with the musical backdrop of "Amazing Grace," "Change is Gonna Come" and "His Eye is on the Sparrow," Thomas Elliott, husband, father, and escaped slave, was eulogized. Other descendants in attendance were Laberta Greenlea, Rochester, New York; Pauline Copes Johnson, Auburn, New York; and Geraldine Daniels, Rochester, New York.

The family of Thomas Elliott will be forever grateful to Superintendent Ricky Bartlett, Willard Drug Treatment Center; Craig Williams, New York State Museum; Peggy Ellsworth, Romulus Historical Society; Gunter Minges; Reverend John Kotun; Sehl Burns, Burns Funeral Home; Herson Funeral Home; and Ithaca Monument.

CHAPTER TWELVE

—

Born Free

Mary felt a strange mix of gratefulness and sadness. The house was quiet and dark. Phillip and the three youngest children were now fast asleep. Mary went to the bedroom and slipped into bed next to her husband. She cried herself to sleep, as she repeated, "Lord, have mercy. Lord, have mercy. Jesus, I trust in thee."

Morning came quickly, and, as usual, Mary was drawn to the John Brown Home for the Aged. She had worked there for several years as a matron, laundress, and cook. There would be much work to do now that Aunt Harriet was gone. Phillip, her husband, was already up and out early. His business required that he feed and water the horses and load the wagon with dry goods and parcels to be delivered before dawn. She had fleeting thoughts of her older children, Harriet (named after Aunt Harriet), Mary, Richard, and Jennie, who were old enough to be out on their own. Richard and Jeanette lived and worked in Auburn.

Harriet and Mary were both married. Harriet married her childhood sweetheart, William Waire, and was living in New Jersey, and Mary was now Mary Gaskin Walker. She and her husband, Henry, lived in Harlem, and then in Bronx, New

York. Black folks traveled from city to city following work. The adult Gaskin children were no different. Many folks were drawn to the big cities in the hopes of finding better jobs. Her younger children, Rose, Phillip Jr., and Lyda, still enjoyed the comforts of home. However, Rose would soon marry Richard Paul Nelson and leave the nest. The young couple had their sights on moving to Syracuse, New York. There was a growing hotel business there.

Whether it was in Auburn or other cities, the work for Negroes was predictable. Colored men provided for their families by working long and hard as day laborers, coachmen, landscapers, chauffeurs, and teamsters. Their wives accepted their station in life, working tirelessly outside of the home as servants, cooks, laundresses, chambermaids, moulders, or seamstresses. Mary thought about how slavery had missed her by one generation, yet her people still held the same positions as the slaves did a generation before her. She often worried about how her children would fare in the world, but she always had a prayer of gratitude in her heart. She was grateful that she and her children were born free. She and her family had escaped the pain, suffering, and separation of slavery. Her grandaunt Harriet, the greatest Underground Railroad conductor, was responsible for that. Harriet rescued Mary's mother, Ann Marie, and other family members from the jaws of slavery. Harriet delivered them safely, and secured their freedom in St. Catharines, Ontario, Canada. Mary was grateful to her mother, grandmother, great-grandmother, and all of her other ancestral mothers who had survived the most hideous form of human bondage. Knowing that her heritage was tied to a great African tribe strengthened her.

We were of the Ashanti people. They were aggressive,

brave, strong, and heroic. These courageous people fought the slavers and colonizers in the Kumasi Region of Ghana, West Africa. They would not give up on their people or their land. Mary knew that her aunt Harriet told family and friends that the old slave women on the plantation always referred to her as one of those Ashantis. The Green, Ross, Tubman, Stewart, Elliott, Gaskin, Stokes family saga began across the Atlantic Ocean, on the Gulf of Guinea, in Ghana, West Africa.

Knowing that this book would lead to the slave experience that began in Africa, my daughter Michele and I wanted to further understand our roots in order to create a realistic story about Modesty, Harriet Tubman's grandmother and my great-great-great-great-grandmother. In the spring of 2006, I was pleasantly stunned when Michele informed me that several prominent Syracuse women would make that dream come true.

Kathryn Ruscitto, Anne Messenger, Margaret Ogden, Vicki Brackens, Kathy Goldfarb-Findling, and Nancy Bottar championed a fund- and friend-raising effort that resulted in a wonderful community effort to send us on a historic trip to Ghana, West Africa. Michele coordinated the project, which was aptly named "The Proud Heritage Journey to Ghana." We are forever grateful to the more than sixty people and businesses that contributed to the Heritage Project, which was administered by Mark Wright from the Cultural Resources Council. Kwame Otieku and Emmanuel Awuah from the Ghanaian Society of Central New York and Doris Danchi, managing partner with Ameriprise Financial, also assisted us. They freely gave their time and personal connections to secure travel arrangements, lodging, tour guides, and an itinerary for our trip.

One year later on March 3, 2007, we left for the trip of a

lifetime. Michele and I were bound for the motherland. Our friends Arethea Brown and Vivian Holmes, who wanted to share the experience, accompanied us. Lori Covington traveled with us as the photographer. The Gifford Foundation made her trip possible. We left John F. Kennedy International Airport on a North American flight that arrived in Accra, the capital of Ghana, just in time for the national celebration of Ghana's fiftieth anniversary of independence from Britain.

As we slowly descended through the clouds, the land beneath us became clearly visible. We all peered through our windows in anticipation of what awaited us. The expanse below appeared to be very arid with sparse vegetation, sandy strips of road, and small buildings scattered throughout the scene. As we disembarked from the plane, I felt exhilarated and humbled to have arrived in Ghana. My eyes could not rest. They found something to behold at every turn. We were welcomed by a group of young African military personnel. Young men and women dressed in fatigues nodded in acknowledgment of our arrival, and wide smiles brightened their faces. As we walked across the steamy tarmac toward the terminal, a feeling of gratefulness enshrouded me. With great anticipation, I looked forward to each new moment and each successive day of our Proud Heritage Journey to Ghana.

I met so many wonderful people who made our stay uniquely memorable. When we arrived at the Hillview Hotel, our new African friends greeted us by saying, "Akwaaba." This was followed by an enthusiastic, "Welcome home." Mr. Joseph Nyarko and his wife, Janet, made us feel very much at home, and Emmanuel Tetteh, our tour guide, took our luggage and showed us our rooms. We were also introduced to our driver, Muhammed, and our server, Joseph. No matter how insignificant, our every need was taken care of. We looked forward to our daily meals. We started each morning with continental breakfast in our rooms: fresh white bread with butter and fruit spread and coffee or tea. Michele was astonished to find that brewed coffee was not to be found very often. Instead, she drank Nescafe instant coffee that she stirred into a cup of boiling water. She learned to live with it. In fact, she brought several packs of instant coffee home. Our lunches and dinners were usually served buffet style with an array of fresh fruit, red peas, rice, spinach casserole, fresh fish, grain-fed chicken fried to a golden brown, and stewed beef. Along with bottled water, juice, or soda, African brewed beer could be ordered. The food was delicious, but I have to admit that I was somewhat disappointed that two of my favorites—wheat bread and Diet Pepsi—were nowhere to be found. We were pleasantly surprised to be taken to a Chinese restaurant; we ordered our favorite fried rice, lo mein, chow mein, and fish dishes.

Most evenings, our African American troupe would convene around the pool at the hotel to debrief the day's activities. From meeting with the Honorable Jake Obetsebi Lamptey; to the Great Chief of Akyem Abuakwa, Osagyefuo Amoatia Ofori Panin; to Mrs. Silvia Asempa, head mistress of the Aburi School for Girls; to Nana Osei Boakye Yiadom, Harriet Tubman Monument, we became most informed and emotional about the slave route, the slave castles, and the slave dungeons. That is not to diminish what we learned about the Ashanti people, their royalty, their fight against the colonizers, and the story of the Golden Stool. We learned that we were connected to Ghanaians and the Ashanti people by way of our collective memory, heritage, and culture.

The African slave experience was very much a part of that. The African slave experience was just as treacherous as the African American slave experience. It preceded and included the journey of the Middle Passage. Clearly, only the strongest of the strong survived. Those who survived the inhumanity of the Middle Passage were thrust into a lifetime of bondage on American soil. Until the Emancipation Proclamation, our family on my mother's side toiled as slaves for Southern planters, farmers, and shipbuilders for four generations. They were treated no better than the farm animals. For many, like Aunt Harriet, there came a point in their lives where they would rather risk death than spend another minute in slavery or to be sold farther south. The allure of freedom was well worth the threat of being recaptured or dying in the process of attaining it. The freedom seekers were motivated by a single possibility, and that was the simple reality that other slaves had successfully achieved freedom in Canada or northern states where they could live free without the threat of recapture.

In Africa, I came face-to-face with the stark reality of how my African ancestors suffered. To hear Africans tell the story of slavery from their perspective helped me to better understand what it did to the continent, to my ancestors, and to their descendants. I felt as though I found a piece of myself that had been missing. My journey to the motherland was an opportunity of a lifetime, and I hope to return to uncover more about my ancestral heritage.

Part Three

—

FORTITUDE

CHAPTER THIRTEEN

—

Gold Coast to the Eastern Shore

Who was the young Ashanti maiden? She was an African girl born in Ghana, on the Gold Coast of Africa. She was captured from her village in the 1780s along with hundreds of other West Africans. Her captors were slave traders associated with the English Royal African Company. The British (as the Portuguese and the Dutch had done before them) dealt in the inhumane business of supplying African laborers to white plantation owners in the colonial states of North America, South America and the West Indies. This young girl who belonged to the Ashanti people from the Kumasi Region was uprooted from her family and homeland. The devastating effects of slavery weakened her village, because by capturing the young men and women, only the elders and children were left to carry on the language, customs, and traditions. The African girl was deposited with hundreds of others in the dungeons at Elmina Castle. The towering edifice rose high amid the stormy surf of the beautiful Gulf of Guinea. The young maiden from the Dark Continent was soon to be catapulted into a life of bondage in the New World.

The black girl was shackled and tortured by the abductors. When she and the others from Kumasi reached the holding camp near Assin Praso, the moans and groans of those who had already been captured were deafening. The more they groaned the more the captors tried to whip them into silence. The African girl screamed and struggled against her abductors. They fought with her, but she was powerless to fight back. They had chained and shackled her by the neck, hands, and feet. Without regard for her femininity, one of the white men took her by the hair, yanked her head backward, and spat on her. The stench emanating from him, and the others like him, was fetid and offensive. Her nostrils flared in disgust. These muscular, odorous bullies were ugly and mean. They corralled and punished the captives with the help of Africans who they had charmed with guns, jewels, spices, and alcohol. These luxuries were often the bait for the betrayal of their brothers and sisters, because they could sell these rare items for a handsome price to the Nanadom (royalty) of the native peoples. Filled with hate and frustration toward the savages, the traders and their African comrades inflicted tortuous treatment to insure the complete submission of the captured Negroes. Shuffling in pained unison among the masses of black humanity, the young African girl dragged her bloodied body to the next stop on the slave route, Assin Manso.

The sounds of the human shuffle rang in her ears. As far as her eyes could see, she took in the agonizing sight of hundreds of Africans making their way to the Manso River. There, one of the slavers towering over her, laughed raucously at her anguish. She could not understand what he was saying, but from the contorted look on his face she knew it was demeaning. The white man put his face in hers. Her teary eyes met his. Terrified, the girl was wondering what would happen next. Her mind flooded with memories of her family. Had they taken them, too? Were they in the village praying to the gods for her return? Will she ever be reunited with them again? Her mother's sweet face lingered in her mind. The girl's thoughts were broken by a white man shoving mush into her mouth, much of it dropping to the reddish-brown earth below. The mixture of boiled red peas and yams did not satisfy her hunger, or quell her fear, anger, and humiliation.

Neither she nor the others were given time to fully digest the mush before they were prodded along to the riverbank. The men and women were separated. White men and African men stood guard as groups of ten to twenty slaves at a time were escorted into the river's waters. For the first time in weeks, their aching, bloody bodies felt the cleansing and healing power of water. The water caressed and glistened upon their black bodies, and it soothed yet painfully stung the raw skin beneath their iron shackles. After each group was allowed to bathe, the slaves were led back up the embankment. Their sun-dried, ashen skin was made soft and subtle again as the traders doused them with red palm oil. Their eyes, ears, mouths, and teeth were examined. Off in the near distance, screams could be heard as hot irons were firmly pressed against each slave's black skin to mark them as the property of a particular plantation owner. Their newly burnt skin had the same distinct brandings of the cattle owned by white men in the New World.

Only the strongest of the strong could have survived the slave route from Salaga to Assin Manso. Cleansed, oiled, and branded, the strongest of the strong shuffled through the last leg of the journey. Weakened slaves were left to fend for themselves in a place they did not know. Others who were near death were thrown into the woodlands to die or to be eaten.

These tortured human beings were of no use to the traders. Their unanswered cries for salvation were unbearable. The Africans deemed fit for the rest of the excursion were herded down a dirt road that led to the majestic military fort in the Cape Coast town of Elmina. The slaves were now only a week away from an even more devastating experience at the dungeons of Elmina Castle.

Days turned into nights many times over. The familiar clashing and clanking of metal sang out as the human shuffle continued. The captives could smell the ocean as they neared the small fishing village. The coast abounded with clusters of coconut trees; each tree bore bushels of the round, green-skinned fruit. Their gigantic palm-like fronds swayed gracefully in the sea breeze. To the left of the dirt path, the captives could see and hear the massive rolling waves of whiteness crashing against the shoreline. Off in the distance, their eyes were transfixed on the largest structure they had ever seen. Its hugeness boggled their minds. Fear of the unknown settled well into the depths of their souls. The strident din of metal against metal announced their advancement toward the huge white castle. The dungeons awaited them.

The throng of captives was led up the retractable wooden planks and through the courtyard, located above two exterior moats that surrounded Elmina Castle. Above the courtyard on the second level of the castle, the noses of several cannons pointed outward to the waters of the gulf. The fortress was aptly protected from the takeover of pirates and other seaworthy enemies. The African slaves were to be protected at any cost.

The female dungeon was dank and small. The African girl and about 200 other young women were held there until it was time to be transported across the Atlantic Ocean. The male dungeon held twice as many of slaves. In comparison, neither of the damp, dark prison cells was better than the other. The cavernous holding camps beneath the castle saw millions of African slaves pass through its confines over the past 300 years. Here, the captives were held in squalid conditions before being transferred to slave ships destined for the New World. The cells were death camps that offered the prisoners no personal space. Indeed, the captured slaves were packed together with no concern for their individual comfort, emotional health, or physical well-being. The dungeons were a stable of sorts that housed the suffering and abused would-be ancestors of Africans who would be enslaved for generations in North America, South America, the Virgin Islands, and the Caribbean Islands.

The Ashanti girl, like many of her sisters, was the strongest of the strong. Thousands of other captives before her died as a result of the capture and abuse. African men and women succumbed from hunger, the ravages of torture, or were killed during unsuccessful attempts to escape. The African maiden, though, was Ashanti. She was the daughter of a warlike, aggressive people. She was able to survive this horrendous assault on her person, her humanity, and her heredity.

The African girl was afraid in this cool, damp, and putrid place. The women were left to live in their own excrement, urine, and blood from menses. The odor was enough to take one's breath away. The only light and fresh air streamed through a small opening about twenty feet above. The orifice was so tiny that even the smallest man or woman would be unable to escape through it. It took all of the mental and physical strength one could muster to survive such inhumane conditions. The girl cried until the tears flowed no longer. She endured the experience and feared it was an example of what was to come. She was distraught, knowing that everything had been taken from her—family, friends, culture, religion, language, and a sense of belonging. The girl was separated from the tribal people, familiar places, and the things that she valued. Grief stricken, she fell to her knees. Tormented, she mouthed goodbye to her family. In Twi, her native tongue, she lamented, "Abusuafo, me ne mo adinkra. Mo ne nyame ntra nkosi awie!" Ghana, the place of her birth, would be forever imprinted in her memory.

Looking up through the small opening overhead, she saw many sunrises, sunsets, and moons. She lost count of the days and nights that had passed into weeks. Each day merged into one unending mix of time. During those many days and nights, she was shaken by the daunting reality of this catastrophic experience. The roots to her homeland had been severed. Everything was lost to her now, even her name. The only thing left to do was to survive. At dusk, she and the others were routinely led into the courtyard, where the governor would ogle them and point his long, slender finger at the beautiful black slave girl who would satisfy his sexual appetite for that evening. While a young African maiden of the white man's choosing was washed and fed and made presentable for the evening rendezvous, the man's white wife was safe and secure and being treated with dignity in their European villa or mansion in a distant part of the world. Not an evening went by without the governor and his men having their way with the chosen one.

After what seemed to be a lifetime, the door to the dungeon suddenly burst open and an abundance of fresh air and sunshine embraced the Ashanti girl and other female slaves. The women gasped as they tried to take in the large amounts of the fresh air. The overseers herded them, one by one, through the barred gateway that was properly named the Door of No Return. Never again would the African maiden or the other slaves enjoy the love of their families and the sense of belonging with their people, or hold dear the safety and security of their motherland.

White men with eyes the color of the ocean, took them aboard small boats and whisked them out to a slave ship anchored a short distance away. Shackled to each other by hands, legs, and necks, the human cargo shuffled along the wharf and then onto the vessel. The captives were crammed into the ship's hold. The Africans had no idea of the horrors of the Middle Passage that were about to be experienced. Could there be anything worse than the journey along the slave route and the inhumanity meted out at the dungeons? The fifty-day voyage across the Atlantic would be yet another unforgettable inhumane experience.

African ancestors of blacks scattered across the Diaspora were packed as tight as canned sardines. Men were chained to each other on one side of the ship, and the women were shackled to one another on the opposite side. They were laid like planks of wood on the floor of the vessel. There was no room for movement, and breathing in the pungent air almost suffocated them. Treated like animals, the captives laid in their own bodily waste—feces, urine, blood, and vomit. There were numerous dead bodies chained to weakened slaves. Chances for survival were made grimmer by the pestilence of small pox, flux, and dysentery. Many tried to take control of their lives, not knowing what the future held. Under the threat of these dire circumstances, some tried to commit suicide by starvation. Others jumped ship, chains and all, to escape the traumatic nightmare aboard the vessel. Death seemed a welcome comfort to them. The remaining captives clung to life and feared the New World.

A significant number of the captives survived the dreadful voyage of the Middle Passage. The African girl was one of them. She endured the monstrous conditions and survived not only because of her faith in the gods, but because of her intestinal fortitude and strength of inner spirit.

The pathetic, life-wrenching experience finally came to an end. Emotional and painful memories continued to plague the young African girl. The moving vessel came to a halt. Many in the ship's hold felt relief, hoping that the hunger, pain, suffocation, and whippings were over. Some thought they had reached a place where perhaps someone would save them. Others felt that they could not continue to live under these deplorable conditions and would rather die. Regardless of their thoughts or desires, they had no control over their physical person—only the slavers did. The slavers began to unload and prepare the human gold for auction. Sparsely clothed, scared, bloody, angry, smelly, and filthy, the shackled slaves were led sobbing and stumbling from the ship to the auction area on the Eastern Shore of Maryland. Shaking and crying, the young Negro girl was dragged along with the others to the main market place, where they would be sold to the highest bidder. But they had no idea that they would be purchased and used like farm animals for the rest of their lives and brutalized physically, sexually, psychologically, and spiritually.

The human cargo was unchained and again rubbed down with red palm oil. They were then led to the white man. He paraded the shackled mass of blackness to the auction block. Many white men were throwing up their fingers indicating how much they were willing to pay. The auctioneer shouted, "Africans for sale."

"You, Suh. You will be this African's first owner, Suh. She is one of those pure Africans. You can have her at a bargain price. Young she is, good and healthy, and she will be a good breeder, too. She can birth for you a litter of chattel that will fill your pockets to the top."

Scared and feeling faint, the African girl knew somehow that the gestures and the shouts of the white man were now focused on her. Nervousness ran through her aching body as the sweat moistened it. A tall white man offering the highest bid approached the auctioneer. He had decided to purchase the African girl. She appeared to be healthy, strong, and controllable. She would make a good house servant. A white man named John Green finalized the purchase. The young slave girl was one of over six million Africans that arrived in North America between 1700 and 1810.

Elmina Castle in the seaport town of Elmina, Ghana, West Africa, located on the Gulf of Guinea. Captured slaves were kept in the dungeons beneath the castle. Ashanti people and others from the interior of Africa were held here before their journey across the Middle Passage. (circa 2007)

One of the slave dungeons at Elmina Castle in Ghana, West Africa
(circa 2007)

The Door of No Return: Thousands of slaves exited the dungeons through this very door, never to return to their motherland. The captives boarded slave ships waiting in the Gulf of Guinea. (circa 2007)

CHAPTER FOURTEEN

—

John Green

J ohn Green was a well-established tobacco planter from
Dorchester County. Little did Mr. Green know that he
would find his newest slave quite desirable. She was a perfect
specimen of a young slave woman. She was about five-feet tall
with skin the color of a chestnut. Her dark brown skin
glistened in the noon sun. Mr. Green thought of all of the ways
that she could work for him. She would also make his wife's
life much easier. She would take over for Sarah who was
entering her twilight years. Sarah was a good and loyal slave,
but she had been worked hard and could not be sold for more
than $100. She had to be replaced by young blood. Massah
Green had acquired Sarah from his father as an heir to his
estate. She had been in the family all of her life.

Missus Prudence Green needed all of the help she could
get. She had a large household to keep up. She had to make
sure that the house was kept clean, that food was prepared, and
that her husband's associates were attended to when they
called upon him. Massah and Missus Green also knew that they
were gaining in years—all the more reason they needed a
house slave who could cook, clean, and care for their
household. Massah Green knew that once Sarah trained his

new African slave, she would make a good house slave. And that is exactly what happened.

The master also knew that he would have to name his slave. She had an unassuming nature about her. She was very healthy. Her teeth, when shown, were the brightest white. Her eyes were a deep brown and the whites were clear. She did not have to be broken because she seemed to be accepting of her lot in life. The young slave did not balk or try to cause any disruptions. One evening while sipping brandy on his veranda, Mr. Green decided to name her Modesty.

The slave girl now called Modesty tried her best to take in everything around her. She saw other people who looked like her working very hard in the fields around the property. She was frightened, but she knew that it would not be a good thing to display her feelings. She did not know the language that was ringing in her ears. She was not used to taking instructions from women other than her grandmother, mother, aunts, or sisters. Modesty was confused, fearful, and very cautious. In the Big House and on the grounds, she was accepted and welcomed by the women who looked like the women folk of her tribe. Most of them knew how she felt. They could relate to her feelings of being a stranger in a strange land. In order for Modesty to make friends with her new home and new life of slavery, they would have to show her the ropes. They had the responsibility of teaching her how to act and how to meet the expectations of the massah and missus. Slowly, she would learn the language. Slowly, she would learn how to live as a female slave. Over the next few months, Modesty proved to the master that he made a worthy investment. Although her vocabulary was shallow, she had learned what was expected of her. She was also to learn that the master had designs on her unlike anything that she had ever experienced.

Master Green did not know from where his desire for the black slave came. All he knew was that Negroes were subhuman, and they were only good for the grunt work that they were born to do. These were the values and morals that he was taught. He knew that blacks (men, women, and children) had but one lot in life. Their charge was to be used hard, worked hard without compensation, and bred hard to produce other Negroes to work the tobacco, rice, and cotton fields. He certainly did not expect that he would find himself desiring his latest acquisition. The massah found himself longing for her soft brown skin lying beneath him. He imagined his long, slender white fingers getting tangled in the wooly mass of hair atop her youthful face. He could envision sexual ecstasy with his slave. He had to have her—and he did.

While weeding a garden chock-full of collard greens one morning, Modesty's mind drifted to a place beyond the Atlantic Ocean. Her thoughts took her back to her homeland in Ghana, Ashanti Land, on the Guinea Coast of West Africa. Grim feelings of anger and sadness slowly turned to joyous ones as she remembered the bliss of freedom, the love of her family, and the closeness of her friends. She closed her eyes to remember the sights, sounds, and smells of her village. She envisioned the tribal ceremonies, rituals, and the language that she was now forbidden to speak. Thoughts of her tribal dress and culture conjured in her mind. She could see the tribesmen, draped in Kinte Cloth, dancing and conducting libation ceremonies. They were praising the gods for all good things: family, food, home, and health. She could almost hear the African drums, woodwinds, and raucous laughter of the villagers celebrating happily in unison. While in her reverie, she was distracted by the presence of a tall white man. He stood above her with his hat in his hands, placed behind his slightly curved back. In a low voice he said, "Good day to you." A smile spread across his full, ruddy face, as his bright eyes traveled lightly over her body and locked with hers momentarily. Deep warmth flooded her body. Nodding, she responded, "Mawnin, Suh." Dropping her dark eyes, the young slave girl asked him timidly, "Massah, ya' wonts me to cums to ya' now?" He nodded in the affirmative, and she knew to follow him.

Modesty felt that familiar sense of being controlled and dominated. She felt as forsaken as she had when she was torn from her family and her motherland, which were now lost to her forever. She was weary from trying over and over again to make peace in her heart. Bittersweet memories of her past lingered in her mind. Modesty's thoughts were suddenly thrust into the reality of her relationship with Master Green. She was emotionally overwhelmed. She knew she had no say in this intimate relationship with the white man. She also knew that she was being robbed of her right to choose with whom she could make love to. With great sadness, she accepted her loss of dignity.

The two had many encounters. On this day, the man stood on his veranda. His eyes glued to the bodies of his slaves. She came closer to offer him a cup of sweet tea. He kindly accepted.

He had ordered her earlier to meet him in his sleeping quarters. As she entered the dimly lit room, he embraced her tightly and kissed her wildly. His pink lips parted in pure satisfaction. She removed her muslin dress and then undressed him. Modesty was well-accustomed to gratifying his every desire.

Modesty was back to work in the big house. While on her knees scrubbing the wood floors, she felt heart palpitations and dizziness. This was not the first time that she felt this unusual strangeness from within. Frightened, she breathed deep in the hopes that it would subside. It did. Relieved that her work was nearly done, she quickly finished up. Before retiring to the slave quarters, she walked to the parlor to ask the missus if she had anything else for her to do. With her usual hand gesture, the woman of the house signaled her dismissal.

Weary and worn out, Modesty approached her cabin. Once inside, feelings of relief and comfort embraced her. She moved slowly to the corner of the cabin where she slept. She laid down and wrapped in quilts to keep warm. She realized that she had not eaten, but she was more tired than hungry. It was not long before she fell asleep with thoughts of feeling better in the morning. Modesty arose at sunrise to prepare hominy and hoecake for her morning meal. She ate a few mouthfuls and her stomach began to churn. Nausea overwhelmed her. Not feeling well at all, she went on to work because illness was no excuse for not serving the massah.

Modesty was dusting the furniture when the smell of slab bacon filled the parlor through the opened windows. Again, her stomach felt queasy and vomit rose in her throat. Not wanting to soil the rug, she bolted out the back door and vomited repeatedly. Modesty was relieved once the heaving and retching stopped. Emma, the cook, heard the gagging sounds and rushed to the yard to help the young woman.

Rubbing her back, the cook asked, "Gurl, is y'all awright?" The younger one nodded her head and said, "Yesum, but dat smell make my inside sick." Emma asked her how long had she been feeling that way. The young slave said the sickness came almost every day, since the end of harvest season a while back. Emma smiled and said, "Lissen gal, yaw gone to be birfin' a baby." Modesty was surprised and devastated all at once. She had no idea that all of this sickness had anything to do with having a baby. Emma went on to say, "Betta let the daddy know." In the inevitable clutches of motherhood, and feeling quite alone, Modesty dropped her head and whispered, "What I's gone say to massah?" Neither of them said another word.

Several months passed and Modesty's belly was fully blossomed. Soon she would give birth to a bundle of life. She now had inner peace and joy about the coming of the child. She no longer felt alone. The new one inside of her would soon join her. This child would be the reflection of everything she held dear.

It was an extremely hot and humid evening. Modesty was sitting in front of her cabin and sharp pains shot through her abdomen. The pain was so excruciating that she started screaming for help. Within minutes, Emma and another slave woman named Jane were at her side. They helped the pregnant girl into the cabin. Before laying her down on the straw-filled mattress, they spread an old tattered quilt over it. Leaning over her, Emma helped Modesty to pull her legs back close to her hips. Water and blood flowed out. Grunting and groaning in pain, the crown of the baby's head showed through the vaginal opening. Squeezing Emma's hand, Modesty screamed in agonizing pain. Instinctively, she pushed down hard with all of her might to release the baby and to relieve the gnawing pressure. At her side, Jane firmly massaged the young woman's bulging stomach to help the baby along. Emma positioned her hands under the birth canal to receive the infant. Suddenly, the head appeared, and within minutes, the shoulders, arms, and legs were fully visible. One good smack on its small bottom and the baby let out a piercing cry.

The wailing was a welcomed sound. Emma checked the baby's eyes and its tiny fingers and toes. She announced that the pale-skinned newborn was a healthy baby girl. She quickly passed the baby to Jane for her to wrap the infant in a remnant of cotton fabric. The little one was then placed into her mother's arms. The infant was feverishly sucking her fingers and routing for her mother's breast. Modesty's parched lips parted into a weak smile, as she cuddled her baby. She was mesmerized as she watched her daughter suckle her breast. It was at that very moment that Modesty envisioned her mother's face. Even though her mother was a world away, Modesty felt a powerful bond with her. She longed to be held and comforted by her. Modesty clung to the feisty bundle, and she vowed to keep her close always. The baby girl was named Henrietta. Little did Modesty know that her baby girl would become the mother of Harriet Tubman, the greatest freedom fighter of the nineteenth century.

News of the birth spread throughout the slave quarters. As was custom, the women folk came to visit and brought food or secondhand items they thought she could use. Some came just to see what the child looked like. Through the grapevine, it was widely rumored that the newborn was the child of Massah Green. Modesty did not confirm or deny the rumor. Nevertheless, her silence was betrayed by the little girl's light complexion.

There would be no rest in the big house. Prudence was outraged. She had known of half-breeds being born in a number of households in the area, but she never believed that it would happen in hers. She was disgusted. How dare he bring shame to their home. How dare he lay with a Negro woman and make a baby with her. She was so humiliated. How would she ever be able to face the other wives of plantation owners? The thought of the slaves whispering behind her back was demoralizing. There was no way that that black whore and her husband's half-breed child were going to live on the property. She would not have it. She would not have them be a daily reminder of her husband's infidelity. They must be taken away. She demanded that he sell them post haste.

John Green knew that he had to remove the woman and the child from the premises. He had no real attachment to the child, but he did have feelings for the mother. No, it was not right, but it was what it was. Yet, he could not make any motions to reverse his wife's decision. He had to sell them, so he advertised in the local papers that mother and child were for sale.

Massah Green was not in any rush to see Modesty leave. He had to admit to himself that she was more than a passing fancy to him. The idea that she could be sold to an owner who might treat her brutally was unthinkable. He knew all to well the conditions that most slaves endured. He did not want her to live the rest of her life in fear of punishment or torture. While he received several inquiries about the woman and child, he continued to hesitate. He did not want his wife to become suspicious, so he led her to believe that the sale had taken place. She was relieved, but the damage to their relationship seemed irreparable.

Green decided that instead of selling Modesty and Henrietta, he would send them away to someone he trusted. There was only one man for the task. Atthow Pattison was the most honorable man that John Green knew. They entered into a gentlemen's agreement that stipulated that Atthow would take mother and child on as his own slaves. They would not be sold and would be kept in the family. This was a common arrangement when a child was born between slave and master. It was also agreed that because of the bloodline, Modesty and Henrietta would be given their freedom when each reached the age of forty-five. Without a word or further contact with Modesty, John Green transported the mother and baby to the Pattison Plantation.

CHAPTER FIFTEEN

—

Pattison's Estate

Y ears before he received the young African and her daughter, Atthow Pattison was already recognized as an established landowner on the Eastern Shore of Maryland near Bucktown. Since the 1750s Pattison's magnificent estate was located on the eastern side of the Little Black Water River and was about twelve miles south of Cambridge. While he owned more than 265 acres, only a portion of his woodlands was cultivated to produce tobacco. Pattison's property was so expansive that it was subdivided into several smaller tracts including Crow's Lodge, Crow's Nest, Crow's Island, East Billency, Cabin Branch, Stanford's Range, Locust Ridge, Linckenhorn, among other smaller lots. Title marshes, ponds, and woodlands surrounded the acreage. The wildlife was abundant: geese, eagles, foxes, falcons, and woodpeckers flourished in their natural habitats.

Most plantation owners with this amount of land were quite prosperous and lived lavishly. Their well-built mansions were comfortably furnished, and house slaves served their families. These wealthy white families enjoyed the comforts of the well-to-do. Family time together was spent worshiping, reading, entertaining, and traveling. Many wealthy whites educated their children. The plantation owners controlled the finances, property, and the field slaves. Typically, their wives were in charge of the home, children, domestic needs, and house servants. This lifestyle was rather typical for the upper class in colonial America.

Atthow Pattison, on the other hand, appeared to be rather unassuming. He valued his family and his dwelling plantation, where he and his family resided. Pattison lived a relatively simple and modest lifestyle. The planter kept most of his land in its organic state, so that the beauty of its natural landscaping, winding roads, and native foliage could be enjoyed. He only used a portion of the land that he felt was sufficient enough to provide for his family and to meet his financial obligations. In his mind, the land was priceless, and it was to be kept in the family for generations.

Pattison, like other planters of his day, owned slaves. Modesty learned quickly that the slaves thought Massah Pattison to be a good master. There were horror stories of the brutality and torture inflicted on slaves by their heartless masters and overseers, all of which was to keep the slaves in their place. Even the livestock was treated better than the slaves. There was much work that had to be done on the plantation, but Pattison did not treat his slaves hard.

Modesty missed the Green Plantation, especially Emma and Jane, but she was gradually getting used to her new surroundings. Henrietta, or Rittia, as her mother called her, was getting bigger by the day. While Modesty worked all day in the Pattison's Big House, one of the older women who no longer worked the fields took care of the young girl. Sometimes, the "auntie" would bring little Rittia to the big house to spend a short time with her mother.

Like most slaves, Modesty lived in separate quarters from her master. The slave quarters were situated behind the big house. During the warm weather, the slave cabins were oppressively hot. It was the exact opposite during the fall and winter seasons. Many of the shanties swayed from the strong gusts of coastal winds. The wind whistled as it seeped through the cracks and openings between the clapboards. Many of these dwellings were constructed with one large room and no separate sleeping quarters. There was barely enough space for a large family to eat and sleep comfortably.

Modesty and her baby girl lived in a typical cabin. The hearth, which was located at one end of the shanty, was used for heating her space, as well as cooking and baking. They slept on an overstuffed, straw-filled mattress in the opposite corner. During the coldest months, they slept nearer to the oven and wrapped in several well-worn quilts to keep warm. The air was stifling in the warm months. After a long workday, she and her daughter stayed outside as much as possible. She would cook a simple supper of hoecakes, salt pork, and collards. In her small garden nearby, she planted and harvested collard greens, mustard greens, and dandelions. She had few personal possessions and her home furnishings were sparse, but Modesty enjoyed the comfort of her home.

Modesty was one of several slaves on the plantation. She and two others worked in the Big House as house servants. The other slaves toiled as field hands. The Negroes, men and women, cultivated the soil, planted tobacco, and cut and debugged the huge green leaves. The leaves were then hung to dry. When the preparation process was complete, the dark, stiff tobacco leaves were bundled and readied for market. Modesty and all of the others always looked forward to the end of the day. The changing hues of the bluish skies from day to dusk signaled their release from the overseer's control. The absence of natural light beckoned the end of another arduous day.

When the weather was warm, the slaves anticipated evenings, especially Saturdays, when they could cook outdoor, listen to stories about runaways, and enjoy the Big House gossip. They also shared news learned through the grapevine about their friends, family, and neighbors near and far. On Sunday mornings, most of them walked to a small gathering place beyond their cabins for spiritual inspiration and fellowship. When they returned to the slave quarters, they were again faced with the verity of slave life. The women were catapulted back into their routine of cleaning, cooking, laundering, and tending to their families. There never seemed to be enough hours in a day to get it all done. Mondays always came too soon.

Modesty, Suke, and Minty (a common name for female slaves) made their way every morning to Atthow Pattison's mansion. The Negro women took care of all of his domestic needs. From dawn to dusk, they tended the gardens, hauled water from the well, cooked his meals, baked his favorite breads and pies, scrubbed the floors, laundered the linens, waxed the furniture, and fed the farm animals. Their day was not done unless they had washed, tailored, and ironed his clothes. They also created detailed handmade quilts from remnants of purchased fabric. The quilts usually had a theme and took many months to complete by several pairs of hands. The handiwork was often showcased in several of the well-appointed rooms. There was no relief from the drudgery of hard work. It was a constant reminder of their station in life.

Three years after Modesty and Rittia arrived at the plantation, Master Atthow Pattison had his last will and testament drawn and dated January 18, 1791. Though he was ailing, his memory and understanding served him well. In his last will and testament, he specified exactly how he wanted his property, personal belongings, and slaves to be disposed. There were no surprises; the patriarch left the majority of his holdings to his immediate family. Pattison handed down more than 265 acres of woodlands and his dwelling plantation to his daughter Elizabeth Pattison and his son-in-law William Pattison and to their children, Gourney Crow, Mary, James, and Aesah. Atthow's wife, Mary, and his daughter also named Mary were not mentioned in the will, as they had predeceased him. He did pass on some property to his widowed son-in-law Ezekiel Keene and his children, Samuel and Anna.

As the patriarch of the family, Atthow wielded his power and authority with a strong arm. His will laid out his expectations. He intended to exercise control over his fortune for generations to come. Regarding his land, home, personal property, livestock, and slaves, Atthow was adamant that the family was obligated to sustain ownership of the land and assets by way of lineage and blood. In no uncertain terms, his will stipulated that the grandchildren must marry into the family. If his wishes were not strictly abided by, everything would be automatically entrusted to his first grandson, Gourney Crow Pattison.

Atthow Pattison bequeathed four female slaves to his heirs. He bequeathed Modesty and Suke to his daughter Elizabeth Pattison. He gave Modesty's mixed-race daughter Rittia to his granddaughter Mary Pattison. To his grandson Samuel Keene, he left Minty. The last will and testament specified that the

Negro slave women and their children would serve the Pattison heirs until each slave and her children reached the age of forty-five. For most slaves, these conditions were considered a welcomed gesture of kindness. Slavery for a forty-five-year term at least promised them the hope of being free during their lifetime.

Even though Atthow Pattison was an authoritarian, he loved and valued his family and was considerate of his slaves. In his will, he admonished his grandson Samuel to use his Negro slave and her children kindly. Pattison knew that his grandson had a caustic personality, and he cautioned and advised the young man on the appropriate handling of slaves. The patriarch was confident that it was not necessary to admonish his daughter or his other grandchildren on this matter. In fact, he trusted that they would treat the slaves kindly and would lead by example.

By 1797, Atthow had died, and Elizabeth became the mistress of Modesty. Modesty served the Pattison family her entire life and was buried on the plantation in the slave cemetery. Elizabeth's daughter Mary acquired Rittia. When Mary became of age, she married Joseph Brodess and took a then eleven-year-old Rittia to the Brodess Plantation. Mary was married to Joseph for a short period; he died suddenly. Mary had given birth to a son, Edward. Both Edward and Rittia were taken to a new household on the Thompson Plantation after Mary Brodess married Anthony Thompson. Rittia served both families faithfully. On the Thompson Plantation, she met and married Benjamin Ross. Of their union, nine children were born. Rittia, Ben, and their children were intrinsically tied to the lands of three prominent masters on the Eastern Shore of Maryland. The entire Ross family and other slaves served as the human crutches who upheld and strengthened the social and economic backbone of the Pattison, Brodess, and Thompson Plantations.

CHAPTER SIXTEEN

—

Green Ross Family

Rittia Green, the daughter of Modesty, was born around 1789 and was a mixed-race child. Her blood and lineage connected her to the Green and Pattison families. She was bequeathed to Mary Pattison, the granddaughter of Atthow Pattison. This Negro girl would be enslaved to Mary until she turned forty-five. According to her grandfather's last will and testament, Mary would also own Rittia's children until they reached forty-five years of age. A female slave's children, or her increase, as they were called, took the status of the mother. If the mother was free, the children were also free, regardless of the father's status. If the father was free and the mother still enslaved, the children remained enslaved. This was true for the Green Ross family. Rittia was a slave most of her life. As a young woman, she married Benjamin Ross. Her husband was freed in 1841, which had no impact on the status of their children. Rittia had not been granted her freedom in 1834 as was stipulated in Pattison's will. Benjamin was allowed to purchase Rittia's freedom in 1855.

Over a half-century earlier, Mary Pattison became the mistress of the Brodess Plantation upon her marriage to Joseph Brodess. In keeping with the stipulation in her grandfather's will, Mary married into the family. Joseph Brodess owned 442 acres of woodlands and tobacco fields west of the Transquaking River and less than one mile west of Bucktown, Maryland. The land was called Eccleston's Regulation Rectified. A path known as Green Briar Road that connected the Transquaking River to the Little Black Water River bound the property.

In 1800, Mary Pattison Brodess brought her slave Rittia into the marriage. The Negro girl was about eleven-years-old. Shortly after 1801, Mary gave birth to a boy child named Edward. Mary Pattison Brodess and her son did not have the security of Joseph's love and protection for very long, because he died shortly after Edward's birth. Widowed and left alone to manage the household and property, Mary later married Anthony Thompson on October 11, 1803. She brought her infant son, Edward, and her slave Rittia into the second marriage.

Anthony Thompson's first wife, Mary King, died in 1802 and left him with four young sons, Absolom, Samuel, Edward, and Anthony. Both newlyweds brought children into their marriage from previous marriages, which resulted in two sons being named Edward. When they married, Anthony Thompson owned the largest farm in Poplar Neck, Caroline County. After the marriage, the combined Brodess and Thompson estates totaled more than 1,240 acres. Mary's grandfather Atthow Pattison would have been pleased.

The Thompson Plantation resembled that of a Hudson River painting. The scenery was magnificent. Rambling white clouds melded into baby blue skies. The air was laced with the fragrance of magnolias, dogwoods, and honeysuckle. Crepe Myrtle trees were in abundance. At dusk, Thompson's plantation Big House stood majestically against the amber glow of the sunset. Well beyond the master's estate, the Negroes dwelled in the slave quarters. There, the slaves lived in dilapidated shanties and found comfort after a long, hard day's work cutting timber and harvesting tobacco. Slaves of all shapes, sizes, ages, and complexions occupied these one-room dwellings. Small children could be found frolicking around the cabins.

At age thirteen, Rittia became one of the forty-plus slaves on the plantation. She often allowed remembrances of herself at an earlier age, when she, too, enjoyed playing children's games and was captivated by catching sight of the wildlife that inhabited the woodlands. Childhood was but a fleeting moment in her mind's eye. At an early age, she came to know the demands of slave life. Rittia's mother, Modesty, had introduced her to the importance of being a valued house servant. Modesty trained her daughter to meet the high standards of her mistress. Although Rittia inwardly rejected her plight as a slave, she believed that she had no choice but to accept the role put upon her. She also conceded to the fact that she had arrived at an age when she would soon be united with a man. This was not only expected, it was required. She, like other female slaves before her, would be expected to breed as many children as her body could produce to increase the master's slave inventory (and also his financial position).

Over the next few years, Rit, as she was called as a grown woman, was moved from working in the house to toiling in the fields. She learned to chop, stack, and dry tobacco leaves. When dusk arrived, the sound of the overseer's horn signaled that the workday had ended. She and the other slaves, exhausted from the rigors of the workday, lazily sauntered toward the slave quarters. Once the slaves reached their cabins, they took their meals, and then sat outside and spent time together. On one such evening, a Negro slave named Benjamin Ross stopped to exchange greetings with Rit and her neighbors. By and by, Benjamin began to make more frequent visits to keep company with Rit. The young slave girl looked forward to and encouraged his visits. Before long, they were seen on Sundays praying together at the Bazzel Church.

Ben was one of Anthony Thompson's many slaves, and the master was very fond of him. Thompson's man Ben was a faithful and trustworthy slave. He was mainly responsible for fieldwork and hewing and hauling timber. Ben was known to be quite friendly and would help anyone that was in need. Even as a young man, he was a devout believer in God and would put all important things in God's hands. The more time he and Rit spent together, the more Rit's affection and admiration for Ben heightened. Their relationship was respectful and loving. Ben and Rit vowed in marriage to be joined as one and to love and be committed to each other for the rest of their days.

The Rosses, like other slave families, would soon come to know the unrelenting demands of upholding two households for a lifetime. Preference was always given to fulfilling the needs of the master and taking care of his household and the plantation, which left precious little time and energy to nurture their own family. They did the best they could. While the slaves toiled in the fields and woodlands, the elder slave women (or "aunties") watched and cared for the children that were too young for the fields. There was no escape from the drudgery, frustration, and pain of slave life. This was all that slave life had to offer. It was real. It was natural. Just as natural as it was for Rit to announce that she was with child. Slavery did not delay the birth of their first child, Linah. The birth of Linah was followed by the birth of Sophe, and then came Robert.

Between 1808 and 1821, several of Rit and Ben's children were born. All slaves young and old were classified as the property of their owners. Mary Brodess Thompson legally owned Rit and Ben's children. Neither Rit nor her children were forty-five by 1823, so Mary transferred their ownership to her son, Edward. At the same time, he took full ownership of the Brodess Plantation that his biological father, Joseph, owned prior to his untimely death. Shortly after he acquired his slaves and property, Edward Brodess married Eliza Keene. As was customary when two people from wealthy plantations married, the division of slaves took place. Edward took possession of Rit and her children, and Ben remained a slave on the Thompson estate. There was no compunction to worry back then about keeping slave families together. They were only slaves. So, Rit and the children were bound to the Brodess Plantation in Dorchester County, and Ben lived away on the Thompson Plantation in Caroline County.

For many slave families this would have been the beginning of the end. Many lost touch with each other and were never reunited. To be ten, twenty, or thirty miles away from each other was akin to being exiled to another country, especially if the master was not disposed to authorize travel passes. Fortunately, this did not happen with Rit and Ben. Although they lived on different plantations, their family remained intact, as evidenced by the births of their other children. The next child born was an infant girl who was destined for greatness. Her parents, siblings, masters nor the nation could foresee her heroism. Abolitionists did not know that one day she would cross their paths. She could not have known that she would become a national figure symbolizing freedom. The girl child, Araminta, would become the Moses of Her People and the renowned Conductor of the Underground Railroad. Later as an adult, she would choose the name Harriet. Araminta Ross Tubman, granddaughter of an Ashanti captive and the daughter of slaves, would liberate scores of Negroes from the jaws of slavery.

Ben and Rit reared five other children after Araminta was born. The Brodess slave holdings were increased by the births of Benjamin, Mary Ann, Harry, Moses, and Henry. The Rosses were a large and close-knit family. As with any family, white or black, it survived the bad times and reminisced about the good ones. The children were growing older and becoming accustomed to the rigors of slave life, but it was not lost on Rit and Ben that Modesty was growing weary. They tried to visit with her as much as possible, which was no easy feat, since she lived miles away on the Pattison estate. Seeing her routinely was made even more difficult because Rit and Ben also lived on different plantations, so creating meaningful family time together was a management nightmare. But the family made the best of it. Not much else could be done. The Rosses were very grateful when their masters provided them monthly travel passes to visit one another and their aging mother.

Modesty was becoming increasingly frail. Each day was growing longer than the one before it. Any job, whether it was tending to children or hoeing seeds during planting season, was just plain tiresome for the old woman. Most of the time, the little ones were well behaved, but once in a while, they were a bit devilish; however, they knew when to stop short of incurring the wrath of their "auntie." On most days they understood it was better for them to be good to each other, play with whatever they could find, and run like the wind around the slave quarters. To do otherwise caused old Modesty's dark eyes to narrow, her full lips to thin out, and her voice to shriek in disapproval.

In Modesty's advancing years, her owner Miss Elizabeth had lessened her workload. Now, it was her job to watch over the slave children from dawn to dusk. They could get into a lot of mischief. She didn't want to admit it, but her love for the children was undeniable. She loved them like her own grandchildren. Even so, as the days grew shorter, so did her energy and patience with the little ones. Modesty asked her mistress for permission to visit her daughter, Rit. Elizabeth directed the driver to take the old woman to her daughter's cabin on the Brodess Plantation. When she arrived, a gentle breeze brushed her sagging cheeks. She carefully made her way to the door, but stopped occasionally to catch her breath.

Modesty was warmly greeted by her daughter and son-in-law. The grandchildren were huddled together on the other side of the cabin and already fast asleep. It was not often that the three of them shared time together in Rit's cabin. Modesty had been ailing lately, and even on warm seasonable days she felt chilled to the bone. Rit sat her mother near the oven. The embers that had burned brightly in the hearth were now slowly fading to a dim light. Ben stoked the woodpile and added several logs to create a few more hours of warmth. Sitting close to the fire, Modesty's shadowy figure was reflected against the clapboard walls. This image created a strange feeling within Rit that she could not explain. She could not remember ever feeling this way before. There was not much conversation that evening. Modesty nodded off from time to time. The silence that spread throughout the cabin was overpowering. Ben felt it, too. They both searched each other's eyes for answers.

Ben was also feeling weary after a hard day of hauling timber. His thoughts drifted to death from time to time. Pushing those thoughts into the back of his mind, he asked his mother-in-law if she wanted to be taken back to her cabin. There was a pregnant pause before Modesty answered. In a barely audible voice, she said she would very much like to stay for the night. Rit knelt by her mother's side and massaged her legs and feet. Looking into her mother's watery brown eyes, she softly whispered how much they loved her and that she could stay as long as she wanted or needed to. Their home was her home.

Modesty knew that she was part of her children's lives and, of course, they were a big part of hers. She felt comfortable there. Their closeness warmed her heart. Her daughter placed worn quilts on the floor in front of the hearth, and she helped Modesty to lie down comfortably. Sleep came quickly for her. It was about 5:30 in the morning when the overseer's horn sounded throughout the slave quarter. Rit and Ben got to their feet, put on their clothes, and began to eat their meal before heading to the fields. Rit then gazed over at her mother. Modesty hadn't moved yet. She must really be tired out, Rit thought. She bent down closer to her mother's side and whispered in her ear, "Mamma." Rit's heart started pounding wildly as fear enveloped her. She screamed, "Mamma, Mamma!!" Ben was at her side within seconds and whispered in his deep voice, "My Lawd Jesus." Rit's frantic screams could be heard throughout the slave quarter.

Rit lowered her head, as did the other mourners. Sniffles

echoed in the air, along with the heart-wrenching sighs and moans of those left behind. One of the most beloved slaves on the Pattison Plantation was lowered into earth in a land not of her birth and heritage. Holding on to Ben and her children, Rit's mind retraced all the memorable things that she had shared with her mother. Ben, a religious man, led the assembly in prayer. The mourners raised their melodic voices and sang emotionally between sobs. Ben, Rit, and their children clung to each other in their grief. Death was final, yet inevitable. The Rosses accepted Modesty's passing, but they were haunted by another kind of loss—the reality of losing each other by being sold to a distant plantation.

It had happened once before with their beautiful daughters Linah and Sophe, and it could very likely happen again. Massah Brodess was a selfish and heartless person. He sold two of their daughters into slavery further south. Both young women were mothers themselves when they were taken from their husbands and children. What kind of man deliberately leaves young children motherless? Linah was forced to leave Araminta and Kessiah. Sophe was forced to leave her only child, her infant daughter, Ann Marie. The baby was suckling at the breast at the time. The family was devastated and heartbroken. They would never see Linah or Sophe again.

Rit and Ben did everything they could to make sure that their three grandchildren felt loved and safe, given the tremendous void that was left by being separated from their mothers. The children's aunts and uncles also did their share to establish close bonds with their nieces in the wake of their mothers being sold to a far away place. This was the nightmare that Rit, Ben, and their remaining children dreaded. No matter how often or how much they prayed, the fear of separation pierced every waking moment. They sought comfort by being together and praying to God for deliverance. Rit thanked God every day for Ben. He had the strength and faith to hold them all together.

Ben Ross was born in Harrisville, Maryland, near Baltimore, during the mid- to late-1780s. Anthony C. Thompson had purchased him and his parents. In 1805, Thompson owned a plantation known as Mary's Delight. It included Miles End (171¼ acres), Webley (259¼ acres), and parts of Sarah's Neck and Kersey's Ramble. His property totaled a scant more than 560 acres. Early on, Thompson owned forty farms and many slaves, but as the old man's life was nearing its end, he had lost a good portion of his wealth including twelve farms. By then, Ben was one of only twenty slaves who worked the tobacco fields and woodlands.

Ben was known to be a devoted family man and a firm believer in God. He was a man who lived by his word and that of the Lord's gospel. Many did not surpass his physical strength. Ben's solid build was muscularly carved from countless years of cutting and hauling timber. He was not only strong in build and faith, but he also had strength of character. This man consistently demonstrated his commitment and loyalty to his family, friends, and master. Ben's demeanor and influence on others was characteristic of a quiet leader. He was someone that people loved, trusted, confided in, and admired. His greatest demonstration of kindness was putting the safety of others before his own and assisting them in anyway possible. As a slave, Ben lived a life of integrity. It was a life to be envied. It was apparent that his master Anthony C. Thompson also enjoyed a good relationship with Ben.

Although he had lost some of his wealth by 1836,

Thompson bequeathed ten acres of land and sufficient timber to build a house to his man Ben. This gesture was seemingly one of gratitude for Ben's loyalty and five decades of servitude. Having lived through the best and worst of years on the Thompson Plantation, Ben was rewarded with land—man's most precious possession. Land given by a master was seldom done, but it was Thompson's ultimate gesture of acknowledgement for his slave's many years of dedicated work. It was the greatest tribute to exemplify the relationship between this white slave owner and his slave. Although good fortune had been bestowed upon Ben, he would not be able to claim his land or his freedom for another five years. Pursuant to his last will and testament, Thompson mandated that Ben serve his son an additional five years after his death. During that time, the aging Ben would serve at the pleasure of Dr. Anthony C. Thompson, son of the elder. It wasn't until 1841 that Ben would have the rightful satisfaction of gaining his freedom.

After faithful service to Thompson's son, Ben was finally given his freedom and the land, but it was a bittersweet victory. He could not experience true freedom without his wife, Rit, also being free. Then in their fifties, fourteen long years would pass before the Rosses could freely live together in their own home on their own land. During those years, Dr. Anthony C. Thompson hired Ben out to the Stewart family. John Trevillion Stewart, a shipbuilder, bought 202 acres of the Thompson property known as the Kemp Farm. Ben cut and hauled timber to Stewart's Baltimore shipyard, and Stewart paid him a fair wage, which was uncommon at that time.

For years, Ben saved as much money as he could manage. In 1855, he paid Eliza Brodess $20 for his wife. He bought Rit as a white man or woman would have bought a farm animal, bolt of cloth, or glittery trinket. It was the price to be paid for an aging slave woman, wife, and mother. Ben paid it willingly and lovingly, although $20 (even back then) could not compensate for a lifetime of fear, pain, tears, and servitude. Whatever joys Rit and Ben would savor as man and wife, living together in their own home came as they approached their twilight years. However, it would not be long before they would depart from slavery for rest of their days.

The Pattisons, Brodesses, and Thompsons owned the Green Ross family for over sixty years. These three families were intimately tied by blood and marriage, and they owned three of the largest plantations on the Eastern Shore of Maryland in Caroline and Dorchester counties. From the late eighteenth to the mid-nineteenth century, the family lines ran strong, not only amidst the plantation families, but between the slave families as well. The Green Ross family, headed by Ben and Rit, lived between two plantations located miles apart, as was common for slave families. For most of their lives, the Brodess family owned Rit, and the Thompson family owned Benjamin. Both of these family plantations were tied by marriage through Mary Pattison Brodess Thompson, the granddaughter of Atthow Pattison. The land and the white families and their slaves were bound together for generations.

Slavery was an institution and condition of eighteenth and nineteenth century America. It was a living part of day-to-day life. Rarely could anyone escape it. Not whites. Not blacks. However, the road to freedom was paved by white and black abolitionists and traveled by slaves willing to die for it. Ben, his wife, and their children would finally make that journey toward the North Star in an attempt to fulfill their dreams. They would find it in some measure in St. Catharines, Canada, and later in Auburn, New York, in the late nineteenth century. Finally, the members of the family who sought freedom in the North touched free soil and wore their blackness and slave heritage as personal badges of courage.

CHAPTER SEVENTEEN

—

Araminta's Youth and Struggles

At the turn of the nineteenth century, the Thompson Plantation was home for Rit and Ben. Although they would later live on two separate plantations, both slaves worked and lived on the Thompson Plantation from 1803 to 1822. They settled into a life of servitude, eventually married, and raised their young family. As their family grew, Rit and Ben were stretched further and further to meet the demands of the Thompson family, as well as those of their own young children.

Even though Rit had served Mary Thompson since she was a child and Ben had served Mary's husband since he was a young lad, the expectations of the mistress and master did not lessen simply because they were raising a large family of their own. Rit and Ben realized that they had fewer hours each day to attend to every one of their children's needs let alone their own. They were grateful, though, to all be living together on the same plantation. They could suffer a life of slavery with the comfort of knowing they had their children with them. The struggles and pains of bondage did not outweigh the joy of seeing, loving, and touching their little black babies at the end of a long, hard day. Yet there was always that nagging fear in their hearts that the day would come when one of them, or more, would be sold.

With the dawning of each day, the threat of being sold off to distant plantations loomed in the back of their minds. No matter how much they loved each other and their children, the Rosses knew all too well the instability of slave life. This was a fact that they could not escape, no matter how loyal and obedient they were. They dreaded the real possibility of separation.

While Ben hewed and hauled timber, Rit took care of the Thompson family in the Big House. She cooked their meals, cleaned their rooms, laundered their clothes, and tended to their every wish. During those years, she was also responsible for the Brodess boy, Edward, and the Thompson children, Edward, Samuel, Absolom, and Anthony C. Jr. Every minute of Rit's day was consumed with the solicitous care and service to the Thompson family. With each passing year, she was painfully aware that she had precious little time to spend with her own children who longed for more of her mothering.

As the Thompson boys entered their teen years, the Rosses realized that their own children were quickly approaching adolescence. The closer their children came to becoming young adults, Rit and Ben knew that their world would be starkly different from that of the Thompson boys. Samuel, Edward, Absolom, Anthony Jr., and their stepbrother, Edward Brodess, had so much to look forward to: they would each take on their rightful role in the landowner class; acquire a substantial amount of acreage, making them very eligible for marriage; marry a woman with blood ties, and her own claim to substantial land rights; and this would thus perpetuate the blood-marriage cycle of land ownership, slave ownership, and economic prosperity, which would be passed on to their white heirs.

The Ross children, on the other hand, had only slavery and a slave childhood to look forward to. No matter how much they prayed for a better life for their children, Rit and Ben had lived long enough and had seen enough to know that the only legacy they could leave their children was bondage to the fruits of the land. Monetary prosperity would elude them through no fault of their own, but for the fact that they were born with black skin and black blood ties.

It was no surprise when Rit felt that familiar fluttering in her abdomen. It was reminiscent of the same feeling that she had with the coming of her other babies. Her sons and daughters were very strong and robust. If sold or rented, each would have brought the master a handsome sum. So far, the Ross family was remained intact. Ben had been rented out, here and there, but not to far from home. They were blessed; they were expecting another baby. One they would love and teach to live this kind of life. Everything would be just fine, as long as they were together.

Rit knew that the time for birthing was near. The Thompsons knew she would soon be back to care for them after giving birth again. The birth of any slave child was welcomed as long as it was healthy and strong. Boy or girl, the master saw it as a means for increased financial gain. The slave mother simply saw the baby as her child, a little cuddly one to be loved and nurtured and taught, regrettably, about the rigors of slave life. Her hope was to keep the child close and safe. Regardless of the drudgery of slavery, the child had to be prepared to produce and to produce well. Good was not good enough. The child would learn early on that she did not have the luxury of enjoying a childhood. As soon as she could work, she would be required to do so.

The birth of the female child was uneventful. Within several hours, Rit had labored and delivered the newborn with the help of a midwife. This one was a little smaller than the others, but her cry was as robust as could be. She routed for the breast quickly and was easily satisfied. Ben was summoned and arrived after his last haul. He found Rit and the infant sleeping comfortably. As he approached, Rit recognized his familiar smell. Reaching out for his calloused hand, her husband moved closer to her and his new daughter. With a smile on his sweaty face, his misty eyes scanning hers, Rit whispered to him, "We's gonna calls 'ah Araminta."

Ben watched the sleeping babe for a long while. Another girl. His eyes shifted again to find those of his wife's. Together they looked into each other's souls. Without a word, they found each other's happiness and pain. Another child to love equaled another child to worry about and another child born into slavery.

It was a warm summer evening. Little Araminta, later known as Harriet, playfully tossed stones toward the cabin as she waited patiently to hear the familiar sounds of horses hoofs announcing the arrival of her father's weekend visit. Ben made the long trip by horse and wagon as often as he could. His master Anthony C. Thompson rewarded his loyalty and hard work with frequent passes to see his family. Even though the trip to the Brodess Plantation was long and wearisome, Ben looked forward to the pleasure of enjoying his family. He enjoyed the comfort, presence, and love of his wife and children.

In the distance, little Araminta, or Minty, heard the horses' hooves thrashing and wagon wheels grinding against the earth through the briar path. A wide smile spread across the young girl's face, as she ran around the side of the cabin to meet her father. As the wagon approached, he called out to her, "Dere she be, mah lil Minty." He pulled in on the reins to bring the Morgan horses George and Dan to a halt, while yelling, "Whooaaa!" Ben climbed down and lifted Minty; she squirmed and happily giggled. As he gently put her down, he looked toward the cabin and saw his wife, Rit, walking briskly toward the wagon to greet him. As they hugged and kissed in their familiar way, Minty wrapped her arms around them to be part of their reunion. It wasn't long before the other children excitedly clamored to greet their father, too.

Rit stood in front of the hearth ready to remove the cornbread with its fresh-baked aroma filling the cabin. Ben was seated at a roughly hewn oak table, which he had hand-carved several years before. They could both hear their children teasing each other playfully outside. Rit, still standing near the hearth, wondered how her husband would react to Araminta's being hired out. Young Master Brodess had come to the cabin days earlier to inform Rit that he was going to rent Minty to Susan Dawson who lived about ten miles away. Brodess often hired out young slaves to make money. This practice was customary for many slave owners.

Rit sat opposite Ben at the table. She reached over and touched his hardened earth-colored hands and squeezed them affectionately. Looking into his probing eyes, she explained Brodess' plan for their daughter Araminta. Ben angrily pushed himself away from the table and found himself in the doorway. Anger, frustration, sorrow, and sadness overwhelmed him. Ben watched as his children frolicked, knowing that they were oblivious to what was about to happen. He was reminded of his powerlessness to protect his family from estrangement and separation. As he turned toward her, Rit could feel the hurt in his pained expression and felt helpless to comfort him.

Inside their cabin, several hundred feet beyond the master's home, Rit and Ben were sullen. Their hearts ached knowing that the talk through the grapevine confirmed the reality that their little girl, Araminta, was going to be rented by the master. Ben paced the floor, while Rit stood in the door well of the one-room enclosure. Neither could speak. No amount of words could express their anxiety and impending sense of loss. Little Minty would be hired out at six years of age to work as a housekeeper for Miss Susan Dawson. Miss Dawson lived miles away along the Chesapeake Bay. Little Minty would soon learn the demands and desires of the white mistress.

At this early age Minty was thrown into childcare, domestic work, and weaving and monitoring muskrat traps. This was commonplace for slave girls. The young slaves were aware, early on, that they, too, were an important part of the slave economy. Their work, whether in the homes of slave owners or in the gardens or fields, was demanded of them. Slave children were also painfully aware that their world seemed starkly different from the one that white children lived in. They learned early on that their days of playing and fun times were few, and that they would spend many days, in fact, the rest of their lives, toiling for the white folks. There would be no time to be tired or restless or sleepy. They would miss much of their childhood, while white children would relish theirs. They, like Araminta, realized that their blackness kept them locked behind the door of inequality. Few slave children realized, though, what society would mete out to them in adherence to the institution of slavery.

Araminta's mother tried to prepare her as best she could for the work that would be expected of her daughter. Rit instructed her on proper behavior, attitude, and communication with masters, mistresses, and their children. She impressed upon her the role she had to play, and play well, in order to escape punishment. Little Minty's mind was full, and she wanted to escape for a while. Her mind would not focus, but she tried intently to concentrate on the rules. She found her thoughts taking her to the woodlands where she loved to play, watch for colorful birds, and listen for her favorite animal sounds.

Minty heard the clamor of horses' hooves in the distance. As the sounds neared, rickety noises from the wagon followed. Nervousness set in. She and her parents walked apprehensively outdoors. They huddled closely in front of the cabin, which leaked badly and had no windows. The horse-drawn wagon pulled to a stop. The woman driver ordered the child to climb into the wagon and to sit in the rear. Her father lovingly lifted her and swiftly situated her according to the woman's instruction. Before the three of them could hug and whisper, "I love you," the wagon lunged forward. Crying without restraint, Minty watched her parents become smaller and smaller before finally disappearing in the morning sunlight. Her parents stood shaken by the inevitable. Sadness pierced their hearts and hot tears flowed from their reddened eyes. Angry and inconsolable, Rit and Ben were powerless to save their little girl from the harsh reality of bondage.

Having left her family behind, Araminta finally arrived at the home of Miss Susan Dawson. Her first domestic experience soon proved to be a brutal one. The young girl repeated the rules over and over again in her head. ("Negroes are ruled by white people." "Negroes have to do whatever white people say.") Not fully understanding why, she knew that she could not afford to make any mistakes. Too often she had seen the telltale signs of raised welts from whipping, kicking, and slapping disobedient slaves. The thought of being beaten frightened her. Araminta's reveries were cut short by the shrillness of a woman's voice. The mistress was summoning her.

"Do you hear me?" the white woman frustratingly yelled.

"Yessum, I duz," Araminta swallowed hard. Her downcast, black eyes swelled with tears. Suddenly, the woman advanced toward her with a raised hand and yelling, "What did I tell you to do?"

Before Araminta could respond, she felt the pressure and pain of the hand across her small cheek. In due course, it left a hot imprint swelling in place. The young girl was stunned and stood quite still in the hopes that the woman would not be further infuriated by the gush of tears streaming down her face. Miss Dawson, undaunted by the show of emotion, continued to spew out a litany of instructions. Araminta wanted to remember the instructions well to please her mistress.

"You will clean the house, dust the furniture, sweep the floors, scrub the walls, and take care of the baby. And, if it's not done right, you will get beat and get another taste of this and worse," the mistress said while raising her hand.

Araminta had often helped her mother clean the cabin, but her small girlish hands were not as efficient in doing the job, as a woman's hands would have been. Before her first day with the Dawson's had ended, she was again brutalized. She had not met the expectations of Miss Dawson. It was the mistress' mission to whip obedience and perfection into Minty, and the woman didn't think twice about whipping the black girl across her neck, shoulders, and back for the least transgression. The excruciating pain of the open wounds was almost too much for the child to bear. Frightened and complacent, Araminta tried for hours to make her small hands create the perfection demanded of her.

Miss Dawson was characteristic of many slave-owning women. She viewed slaves as subhumans who needed to be beat into submission. She seemed to take delight in abusing the young slave; the violence was relentless. During her stay there, Minty was made to do many jobs without complaint. Sweeping, dusting, and scrubbing were everyday routines, as well as tending to the Dawson baby. She cradled the baby and rocked her many times during the day. Each night, Araminta rocked the child to sleep for fear that it would cry out. If the child cried and awoke the mistress, Araminta would be lashed without mercy. Minty would often weep uncontrollably and pray that the infant would sleep peacefully throughout the night. Minty fell asleep many nights only to thrash about restlessly, dreaming about the mistress reaching for the whip. Even in her dreams she could feel the excruciating pain of the rawhide slice into her black skin. The dream always ended (as it did sometimes in real life) with the mistress' sister intervening and persuading Miss Dawson to let her train Araminta. Hearing about the cruelty that Minty was encountering, Rit begged the master to let her daughter return to slave row.

Things were not much better at the Cook residence. Mrs.

Cook was determined to force Araminta into learning how to properly weave. There was a small room set aside in the house where weaving was done. Minty was uncomfortable in this room. It was tiny, stifling, and filled with bundles of yarns, fabrics, and threads. In the corner near a small window was the loom and chair. The stagnant air was musty. Many white women took on weaving to furnish their own clothing, as well as to supplement the family income. In many households like this one, the slaves were deployed as artisan weavers.

Mrs. Cook was faced with the young slave's reluctance to master the art. Araminta much preferred to be outdoors with the sun and the light breezes brushing against her cheeks. She longed to swing a hoe and dig up the earth to prepare it for seed. Minty imagined a sense of being free like a bird and being in charge of herself even if only on that small plot of earth. She also daydreamed about working in the gardens and collecting herbs and healing plants in the woods, as her father had taught her. Her dreams and desires were rarely fulfilled. She had been hired out once more to a woman who demanded and expected of her the work performance an older slave woman. Brutality was never far away.

Araminta's mind raced wildly. She knew that she did not want to be indoors doing these boring tasks, but she also knew that her mother had explained how slaves, even children, were to behave to avoid severe punishment. Even though her thoughts pressured her to obey and learn, her spirit was not cooperating. Her body language betrayed her. Araminta's obvious reluctance and belligerence enraged Mrs. Cook. The white woman was in no frame of mind to indulge the whims and fancies of the slave girl. Not only would Minty weave, she would also be responsible for monitoring the muskrat traps.

Little Minty dreaded the mornings. Before settling down to weave, she began the day by wading in the murky creek nearby. Chills ran up and down her spine while goosebumps sprang up on her thin arms as she slowly moved her feet along the sludgy creek floor. It was filled with water-loving insects and other small animals that nipped at her feet and ankles. Other creek inhabitants would teethe on her calves and upper thighs. The poor girl could barely monitor anything, let alone the muskrats, for the constant swatting and scratching of her hands, arms, and legs. Nevertheless, she knew what would happen to her if she did not monitor those traps precisely as Mr. Cook had shown her.

Araminta had soon become deathly ill. Of course the Cooks believed the belligerent child had brought the illness upon herself. When word reached her mother, she begged Master Brodess to allow her daughter to be brought home. With some reservation, Edward Brodess agreed, and Araminta was delivered to her mother's cabin. One look at the child and Rit knew she had developed a severe case of the measles. Rit was furious and concerned all at once. She sent word to Ben through the grapevine. Together they began to nurse their child with plants, herbs, and potions that Ben knew would speed the healing process. Her parents consistently prayed at her side. Within several weeks, Minty was well again.

CHAPTER EIGHTEEN

—

A Blow for Freedom

A raminta had no interest in working in the Big House owned by Edward Brodess. A teenaged Minty found great pleasure working in the open fields. She would much rather work there with her hands in communion with the earth, cutting tobacco leaves and preparing the gardens for seeding. She particularly enjoyed showing strength and skill with the plows. It was exhilarating when the sun bathed her chestnut-colored skin and light winds kissed her cheeks. Araminta felt a sense of freedom as she worked and sang the songs from church. As her contralto voice filled the air with "Go Down Moses," the slaves nearby lifted their voices in unison. If one didn't know better, you would think they were singing in the Bazzel Church where Araminta's father often preached.

Araminta and the other Negroes gathered their tools before finishing up for the day. Dusk was setting in on this early fall evening. Minty's head was wrapped in a damp white rag. Her crinkly, dark hair peeked out from underneath it. She wiped the sweat off of her forehead with the back of her roughened, dark hand. Her full lips were nearly parched, and her small yet muscular frame ached from the day's toil.

Araminta lazily placed a hoe in the crook of her shoulder as she readied to leave the field. Her eyes suddenly fell upon a Negro man running speedily from the neighboring Barnet Plantation. As he got closer to the Brodess property, Araminta and the other slaves knew something was amiss. Negroes were not allowed to leave the fields without permission. This Negro was not only running—he was not accompanied or supervised by a white man. Something was wrong. The slaves knew that this man was running off. Some were shocked and others were undecided as to what they should do, if anything. But they all knew that soon a white man would be in hot pursuit.

As fast as his legs could carry him, the slave—Jim—ran along the edge of the fields toward the country store that was owned by the Stewart family. At some point earlier on Jim had heard that the Stewart store would be a safe place to hide. Out of breath and panting heavily, the fear of being caught terrified him. However, the promise of being sold to some distant plantation motivated him more to run from the Barnet farm. Thoughts of being shackled on the chain gang destined for the Deep South made him willing to take the risk of death. Jim did not realize that his overseer Massah McCracken had caught sight of him until he heard his brusk angry voice:

"Niggah boy, where you think you goin? Ahm gonna beat the black off you. You be bettah off stoppin' while you ahead."

Jim could almost feel McCracken's breath on his heels. He ran into the small country store, thinking that if he could just get inside he would be safe. The country store stood along with no other structures around it, but it was not far from the Brodess property line. It was situated at the crossroads in Bucktown, Maryland. The store was a one-story framed building with weathered, yellow paint. There was only enough room inside to hold shelves and barrels of staples that neighboring farmers would purchase. Jim caught sight of the front door. He leaped over the wooden steps and plunged through the door and knocked down bags of wheat and flour as he tried to locate another door from which to escape.

Before he could reach the door leading to the backfields, he felt the horrendous pressure of McCracken's large white hand on his shoulder. Jim's heart was pounding furiously. The white man yanked Jim around and punched the black man square on his jaw. Jim fell to his knees but leapt up quickly enough to land a sharp blow to McCracken's chest. The fight continued. The room seemed to swell with a flurry of arms and legs. Their moans and groans struck a kind of strange melody. Sweat drenched their bodies creating an extremely ripe odor. The white man was trying to keep the black one from leaving; the black one was fighting for his life.

Araminta knew that no good could come of a white man in hot pursuit of a runaway. She knew that the slave would likely be killed or at least severely tortured. Minty and the others were hesitant to leave the fields. They feared the worst possible outcome for Jim. Suddenly, McCracken appeared in the doorway of the store with a stronghold around the black man's neck. The red-faced overseer roared at the slaves gathered nearby.

"You," he said pointing to young Araminta. "Get up here and help me tie this niggah up. Niggahs know you don't run cause we always gonna ketch ya."

Araminta immediately obeyed his instruction and went into the store. McCracken yelled at her again. His tone was insistent as he repeated the command:

"Help me tie this niggah up."

Minty had no intention of helping the white man. Instead of assisting him, she yelled back, "Let 'im go, Massah. Pleeeze let 'im go."

Minty tried with all of her might to break the white man's hold on the runaway's neck. The overseer was stunned and angered by her belligerence. No good heifer. He looked for the first thing he could get his hands on to beat the black girl. He spied a two-pound iron weight. Without hesitation, he lifted the piece and swiftly smashed Araminta on her forehead. Shrieking and writhing wildly, she stumbled while blood gushed from the hole in her head. The blood flowed freely over her black face and splattered on the white man, too. The excruciating pain shot through her head and made its way through the rest of her body. She fell to her knees and laid in a heap on the blood-stained floor.

In that very instant, Jim saw his chance to run. With sadness in his heart, he looked at Minty and felt her pain. He knew that she was trying to protect him. Jim could hardly believe that such a young girl would put herself at risk. He was regretful that he could not return the favor. He ran for the door at the other end of the store and bolted out. The adrenalin coursing through his aching body strengthened his stride.

McCracken stood over the bleeding girl and cussed profusely. Now, he not only had a runaway nigger, but a half-dead one too. These niggers are nothing but trouble, he thought. He felt no remorse for Araminta. She had gotten what she asked for. He beckoned the field hands close by:

"Come in here and tote her over to her mamma's cabin."

The orange sun had begun its slow descent beyond the slave quarters. Several of the field hands carried Minty a short distance back to the cabin. They floundered under her unconscious, limp body. Before long, they approached Rit's cabin. Rit stood in the doorway. Her eyes quickly scanned them. She realized that it was her daughter who was bleeding so profusely. Her clothes were soaked in blood. Her arms and legs dangled like a mauled animal's. She began shrieking loudly as they brought the hurt child in and laid her on top of several quilts in a corner of the cabin. Fearing the death of her daughter, Rit needed to let her husband know what had happened. But Rit knew that the only way to let Ben know about the head bashing was to beg Master Brodess to send word to him.

When Ben arrived, he was devastated and grief stricken to witness his daughter's pain and suffering, especially knowing that he couldn't retaliate against the white man. The only way that Araminta would survive this ordeal was for Ben and Rit to nurse her back to health under God's care. No doctors were ever called to the slave quarters to heal the sick. Her parents immediately began a regimen of herbal medicines harvested from woodland plants. Minty's brothers and sisters quietly watched their father pace the cabin's dirt floor and pray for Araminta's recovery. Ben comforted his children and his wife as they agonized over Minty's malady.

Araminta stayed in this condition for several weeks. The fever was unrelenting and the pain pierced her head and ran through her thin body. This was not the first time that her mother had to nurse one of her children back to health. By far, though, this was the most devastating for her. The healing vigil required her constant cleansing and applying of poultices to the open wound to draw out the infection. Rit was grateful that she had the ability to care for her daughter. She did it all with love and patience.

Rit resented Master Brodess because he showed no sympathy or concern for her daughter. Brodess added insult to injury by deciding to sell Araminta. Rit was enraged and frustrated at the thought of going through the pain and devastation of losing another child. She felt helpless. She knew that she was unable to stop Brodess from selling her daughter. Rit was reliving the tragic sale of her other daughters Linah and Sophe.

After the injury, Brodess felt that Minty was a liability that would cost him, so he decided to profit from her sale instead. He led many neighboring farmers down to the shack to look at Minty—damaged goods. Without warning, Brodess would charge into the cabin with potential traders or buyers. They would examine the girl and shake their heads, as if to say she would be of no asset to them. Brodess soon realized that she was of no value to anyone. He regarded her as a burden.

It took months before Araminta was back to working the fields. The injury left a terrible scar where the almost fatal blow struck her. An indentation on her forehead, slightly above her eyes and nose, would mar her for life. Although she was able to get back to work on the plantation, she suffered from sudden sleeping seizures. She would fall into a deep fifteen-minute sleep without warning, and she would simply resume the activity she was doing when it occurred, as if there had been no interruption. The injury also caused her to appear half-witted or slow at times. She accepted that the blow would affect her life, but it would not keep her from living a normal life in the slave quarters.

CHAPTER NINETEEN

—

A Mother's Challenge

I t was approaching high noon. Rit had worked hard in the field. Her head was wrapped tight in muslin, and her body was draped in loose clothing; her arms needed rest from digging with the hoe. She caught sight of Master Brodess and another man walking toward the field. Brodess was taking the trader to the area where the other slaves worked. The trader was anxious to see what slaves were available for purchase. As they came upon a group of able-bodied slaves, the white man examined them and made off-handed comments as to whether he thought they were physically strong and mentally alert.

The trader's attention was drawn to one particular young male slave. He was muscular, medium height, and chestnut colored. The buyer informed Brodess that he was willing to buy this slave for a good price. As far as he could tell, the slave met his expectations, and he discussed with Brodess the boy's prospects as an excellent field hand and breeder. Brodess was quite satisfied that he was going to make a good sale. The purchase of this slave (and possibly others) would enhance Brodess' dwindling financial situation. He hoped that this sale would be the start of a trend that would help turn things around. He knew that he would eventually have to sell more slaves to stabilize his lost assets.

The strong black male stood rigidly while being handled again by the white man. He could feel the trader's coarse hands roaming over every part of his body. The man looked closely at his eyes to make sure that they were clear and had no signs of illness. He opened the slave's mouth to examine his teeth and gums. He also checked the young man's arms, thighs, buttocks, and calves to determine if he could endure long work hours in the fields. The adolescent male was fearful that he was exactly what the trader wanted and that he would very likely be sold to him. He knew that he would bring a good price.

The young slave's emotions ran amok. He feared that he would be alienated from his family. It was a fear that haunted every slave, and now his fear was becoming a reality. He knew he would be taken away from his family. His reveries quickly shifted back to when his sisters Linah and Sophe were sold. Now his time had come.

Before he could think anymore, he caught a glimpse of his mother a few feet away. He could feel her eyes searching for his. With their eyes locked upon each other's for a brief moment, Rit quickly moved toward her son and shielded his body with her own. She demanded to know what the men wanted with the boy. Without waiting for an answer, she grabbed her son's arm and led him off the field. He was happy that his mother had intervened. Over the next few hours, Rit hid the boy deep in the woods to keep him out of the master's reach. Once she assumed that the trader had left the plantation, she and her son returned to their cabin.

Brodess knew that the mother would eventually take the boy back to the cabin. He also knew that the boy's father, Ben, was living at the Thompson Plantation several miles away. Therefore, there was no time like the present to go back to get the boy. Brodess approached the cabin after sunset, when he knew that the slaves had returned from the fields. He was confident that he would find the boy and his mother there. Brodess and the trader walked hurriedly down slave row and pounded loudly on Rit's door. Fully expecting that the men would come after what had happened earlier, Rit was not surprised or frightened to hear the male voices outside the cabin door. Keeping her son and the others well behind her, she fearlessly appeared in the doorway.

Rit eyed each man up and down, and then asked in an aggressive manner why had they come. Brodess, wanting to gain entry to the cabin, tried to trick her into thinking that they were there for some other reason than to capture her son. He told her that the trader wanted to come in and light his cigar. Rit was in no mood to be taken for a fool. She knew the real reason for their visit and refused to let them enter. The men began to move forward into the doorway. Without hesitation, Rit told them in no uncertain words that she would split the head open of the first one that tried to come in.

Days later, Brodess was heard to have said that he was extremely glad that Rit had reacted that way. Apparently, he did not have the backbone to stand his ground with Rit or the trader.

CHAPTER TWENTY

—

Untimely Love and Devotion

A raminta was delighted that it was time to enjoy the end of her week's work in the fields. She, like the other slaves on the Brodess, Meredith, Stewart, and Thompson Plantations, was allowed to spend some free time with friends and family. The Bazzel Church was one of the gathering places for festivities on Saturday evenings. As Minty walked into the church with her mother, brothers, and sister, melodious music filled the air. Everyone present smiled at one another while looking for their usual seats. Heading for their favorite spot, the Rosses took their places in the middle pew on the right side of the church. The presiding minister was already at the pulpit preaching the gospel. Beautiful black bodies started swaying back and forth and shouting "hallelujah." The service was very special that day because Araminta's father, Ben, was the guest preacher. His message was compelling; the congregation responded with thunderous clapping and boisterous "Amens!"

It was common for the church folks to meet after the service to enjoy delicious foods prepared by the older women. The air was filled with the sweet and savory aromas of ham hocks, chicken, chitterlings, collards, and fruit pies. The tables were laden with everything one could imagine. Hurrying to get in line, Araminta noticed that she was standing near the man who sat behind her in church. He was of medium height and what they called a dark mulatto. They both smiled as they introduced themselves. Their hands locked in a warm welcome. Feeling quite comfortable with each other, each filled their plate to their heart's desire and gazed over to see what the other had chosen to eat. They quickly peered around for a place to sit. Finding seats under the poplar tree, Araminta waved to her parents to let them know where she was. John motioned for Minty to take her seat first. Both enjoyed eating healthy servings of succulent roasted chicken, ham hocks, collards, potato salad, and gooseberry pie. They were so busy eating that they had little time to talk.

"What plantation you from?" John finally asked while finishing the last bite of his meal.

"I is from the Brodess Plantation," Minty responded. "Who is your owner?"

Laughing loudly, his teeth gleaming between thick lips, John said, "I ain't no slave. I was born free."

Araminta stared at him in disbelief. "I don't believes dat."

Shaking his shoulders and laughing gleefully, he teased her. "I am free. Free as the winds blow and the birds fly. You can believe dat."

John shared his family background with Araminta. He told her how his family was freed several generations ago by the Tubman dynasty. He pointed off in the distance toward Parsons Creek and told how he was raised at White Marsh near Tobacco Stick. The Tubman clans lived like royalty and were devote Catholics, but they eventually freed all of their slaves. The slaves previously owned by the Tubmans retained their master's name. This was common practice for freed slaves who had respect and gratitude for their former owners. John's family took the Tubman name in keeping with this time-honored tradition. Just by spending this short time with John, Minty began to feel a sense of care and comfort in his presence. She was not anxious to leave, but knew she had to head back to the cabin. Not knowing quite what to say, Minty lowered her eyes and hoped her new friend would break the awkward silence. In a gentleman-like manner, John suggested that they see each other again. Araminta's heart warmed over as she anticipated the possibility of their courtship. The two of them spent many hours together whenever time permitted.

It became ever more so apparent that John Tubman and Araminta Ross wanted to spend more time together. Minty's parents and the other slaves in the quarter witnessed their growing devotion for one another. The grapevine carried the word that the young couple was to be married. John and Araminta turned rumor into reality when they "jumped the broom" around 1844. Minty was allowed to choose her own mate, since Master Brodess considered her damaged goods.

Although Araminta was married to a free man, it did nothing to change her status. She remained a slave under the control of Edward Brodess. The time that she spent with her husband away from the plantation gave her a small taste of freedom—a taste she much enjoyed. In the time that she was permitted to spend with John, she was not under the same supervision and scrutiny of the overseer and master. Even though their time together was short, she delighted in being able to do what she and her husband chose to do without being managed and controlled. They would often have conversations about their families, their work, and their problems. It became clear to them that there was essentially no difference between his being a free man and she being enslaved. No matter their legal statuses, they realized that their black skin was their badge of inferiority. The effects of slavery, racism, and discrimination were one and the same. The price of freedom could not be paid. The color of one's skin superseded the recognition of a black person's humanity and dignity.

Over the next five years, John and Araminta settled into their life together, accepting its realities and challenges. Nothing was more hurtful and perplexing than their inability to have children. Soon the two would be faced with yet another unforeseen turn of events. On what would prove to be her last visit to John's cabin, Minty tearfully whispered, "John, I hears Missus Eliza is gon' to sells me off." She could well remember how devastating it was when her sisters were sold. Araminta could still recall Linah kicking and screaming as they were dragged away. Her mother and father sobbed and begged the master not to sell them to the chain gang. Massah Brodess could care less about their grave concerns. It was his right and privilege to sell his property whenever it suited his financial needs. He did not need their permission or approval.

It was 1849 and Elizabeth Keene Brodess was in desperate need of money to support her nine children. Her husband Edward had died and left her in financial straits. The only solution was to sell off a number of Negroes, and Araminta was one of the chosen slaves. She tried explaining to John how she felt about the inevitable. Leaving her family, friends, and home behind would be traumatic for her, but it was clear in her mind that she would not be sold to some distant plantation in the Deep South under any circumstances. Her rebellious nature made her unwilling to accept what was now facing her. As soon as she heard that she was to be sold, Minty decided to take charge of her own destiny. She had made up her mind to escape from the Brodess Plantation.

Araminta and John sat in silence, each pondering their next move. At first, John was reluctant to say that her request sounded ridiculous. He knew that if she was sold to some distant plantation, he could do nothing about it, and he would not consider escaping to the North. John had no desire to escape. He would remain free. He loved Minty deeply, but he knew that she would not understand his unwillingness to escape with her.

Reluctantly, John told Araminta, "My family and I been free for years, and I don't want to give that up at no time. I love you but I can't give freedom up, never. I can't goes with you."

Hearing his words, Araminta felt a mix of emotions. Anger, frustration, and betrayal engulfed her.

CHAPTER TWENTY-ONE

—

Freedom Now or Never

O ne fall morning in 1849, Ben was hard at work on the Stewart Plantation preparing a load of lumber for haul to the Baltimore shipyard. He was providing his workhorses with water and oats prior to their journey, when he was summoned by John Trevillion Stewart. As Ben made his way to the Big House, his nostrils filled with the crisp fragrance of the morning air. Ben was nearing the veranda of the Big House, when he caught sight of John T. Stewart conversing with some Negroes that he had hired for field and lumber work.

Ben approached the oversized porch with his usual swaggering gait and passed the other black men as they retreated to the nearby woodlands. By this time, John had taken a seat on one of the wicker chairs. His glance surveyed the glorious view of hundreds of acres stretching as far as the eye could see. John had inherited this land from his loving mother, Elizabeth Fookes Stewart. John and his family lived comfortably on the land. The couple was known to have many overnight guests who were often entertained by Ben's daughter Araminta. (She was known to have extraordinary strength for a woman. By all accounts her five-foot frame betrayed her ability to pull a plough strapped to her strong back.) Minty did not mind entertaining the white folks, in fact, she was proud to be the only woman recognized for her God-given strength.

As Ben walked onto the gleaming white veranda, he considered his good relationship with John Trevillion. John was known to be a good and decent man, and he lived his life as one who valued all men, black or white. Ben and the other Negroes observed how John treated his slaves, his hired help, and everyone with whom he came in contact. He showed respect and dignity for human kind. This was perpetuated as a family value. Although Negroes had not been emancipated, John paid his hired help a decent wage. Ben was paid about $60 a year; his daughter Araminta was also well compensated. Ben knew the day would come when he would have saved enough money to purchase his wife, Rittia. Ben was grateful to work for such an amicable man. This was not the case with Dr. Anthony C. Thompson, the son of Ben's former master. The younger Thompson was a mean-spirited person who treated his slaves cruelly. Stewart, on the other hand, regarded Negroes fairly.

John Trevillion looked up at Ben with a worried look in his light blue eyes.

"Morning, Massah Stewart," Ben said with apprehension.

"Morning, Ben. I've got some bad news about your girl Araminta. She's about to be sold and I reckon your sons Harry and Ben, too. Did you know that?"

"Yes, I hears that. We all hears that. My woman, Rit, is taking it real bad. Her heart almost broke. More chilluns to be took from her. Hurts me real bad, too. Massah Brodess promises my family they freedom after he died, but that ain't gonna happen."

John could see the tears welling in Ben's eyes. Ben, a tall, well-built, chestnut-colored man, was strong and able bodied, but John could see that this conversation revealed a softness in him. John could feel Ben's pain.

"I know this is a hard thing. No man or woman should ever have to grieve over the selling of their children," the empathetic master said.

Both men stared intently at each other.

"You know, Ben, now may be a good time for Araminta and the boys to run away from here. The traders will be here in a day or so. If they stay, they are only going to be sold to different plantations in the South. You will all probably never see them again."

Ben was stunned by John's words, although he was not surprised by his suggestion that they escape. Ben had often heard interesting things about John from other slaves. They not only spoke of his leniency toward them, but some Negroes even told stories about him assisting runaways in their attempts to reach freedom in the North. Ben knew that John was right. It was risky, but his adult children really had no other choice. Whether they were sold or ran away, they would still be separated from the family. Ben felt that he should persuade them to escape. He knew that he had to get to his sons Harry and Ben Jr. who were several miles away working the Brodess tobacco fields. It would be easier to talk with Araminta, because she worked with him on the Stewart Plantation. He would discuss this with her when they returned to slave row at dusk.

Ben's reverie was finally broken when John asked him what he was thinking about. Ben looked at him with sadness in his eyes.

"Thank you, Massah. You a good man. Must be you know

how I'm feeling. I can't tell Rit yet, but I will talk to my children 'bout goin north. If they wants to go, I helps them anyway I can."

John Trevillion did understand.

"You're a good man, too, Ben. Let's talk about how I can help."

A few nights later on the Brodess Plantation, some of the slaves were gathered around the fire in the main yard near the cabins. They used this time to talk about goings on in the big house and other gossip. Ben looked for the right moment to have Araminta, Harry, and Ben join him outside of Rit's cabin. His grown children knew that their father was troubled by something. There was no time to beat around the bush.

"You knows I love you all. I would do anything to keeps my family together, but there's nothing you or me can do. Missus Brodess gonna sell you off. I thinks it best if you get away from here. You got to make your way north. I rather see you try to be free than be put on the chain gang. Me and Massah Stewart come up with a plan," said John.

Silence hung in the air. Minty and her brothers knew that Missus Brodess was going to sell them. Eliza Ann was facing mounting debt and needed the money. Araminta broke the silence:

"This is mo' den I can beleebs. Massah Stewart is gonna hep us leave dis here place? What goin' ta happen to you and him if Missus Brodess find out?"

Ben was confident that they had come up with a good plan.

"Don't worry, with God and Massah Stewart helping, you all can make it."

Araminta and her brothers were having mixed emotions. They knew from stories about other runaways that this was a dangerous undertaking. Some runaways were returned dead, and their mangled bodies were left exposed in the slave quarters to dissuade others from leaving. Still others were returned and tortured, making them an example for those who might be considering running away. Harry, Ben and their sister also knew, though, that there were stories about Negroes who had made it to the North. Just briefly considering the treacherous outcomes, they decided the risk was the price to be paid for freedom.

Now back in the cabin, Araminta was elated with the prospect of achieving every slave's dream. This, however, did not prevent her from being anxious. Thoughts of her sisters Linah and Sophe swirled around in her head. She remembered the tragic day when her older sisters were sold. They were chained to other slaves and dragged away. Their final destiny was a place called the Deep South. Minty promised herself that that would not happen to her. Minty was certain that she and her brothers would find a way to escape the plantation. It would not be easy though. There would be danger and possibly death. She was painfully aware of the obstacles, but she would not let this deter her from seizing the opportunity to gain freedom.

Araminta and her brothers set out to leave around midnight on a Saturday. This was the best time for runaways to escape, because they would not be missed until Monday. They made sure to dress warmly for the journey and to pack enough food and water to last several days. According to the plan, they would meet in the woods on the far side of the Brodess Plantation along the Green Briar Path. The path was covered with twigs, fallen leaves, and broken stones, which caused some discomfort as they trudged along. The night air made them shiver enough to pull on their woolen wraps. The darkness engulfed them, and they could hardly see each other. Their chestnut-colored skin and dark clothing blended into the deepness of the night, so walking closely together was a must. The only light was from the brightness of the moon and the gleaming stars hovering above.

The trio knew that it would be days before they reached their first stop. They traveled the woods for hours before stopping to rest. They were exhausted and needed to relax their tired limbs. Araminta motioned for her brothers to settle down on the stump of what was a large poplar tree. The morning sun would rise soon, and they needed to rejuvenate for the next leg of the journey. The three nodded off in the chill of the fall night air. Sleep came easily.

They were awakened by a beam of sunlight beating upon them through an opening between several large tree limbs. The sun's position alarmed them that they had slept longer than was safe. They quickly needed to continue their trek north. Periodically, they would check the trees to determine which direction the moss was growing. (Moss grew on the north side of trees.) They walked along the woods in that direction, knowing that God's nature would keep them on track.

Araminta and her brothers spoke very little. They were attentive to the sights and sounds of the woods. The trio recognized that they had to respect the home of the wildlife that resided there, but they also had to keep watch for anything unusual. It was well-known that some runaways did not make it to the first safe haven for being attacked or mauled by animals, or captured by patrollers and slave hunters. The more they walked, though, they felt they were coming closer and closer to the Promised Land. But they would not let themselves be fooled. The whites probably already knew they were missing and would be in hot pursuit. Every once and a while, Minty would softly hum an old Negro spiritual to help lift their spirits.

Night had fallen once more. Araminta and her brothers knew that they should be coming upon a clearing by daylight. They searched for an adequate spot in the woods to build a small fire. Harry gathered the wood and kindling. Ben Jr. started the fire; he reminisced about his father teaching him the skill. The warmth of the glowing yellow and orange flames seeping into their bones reminded them of the night fires in the slave quarters. They already missed their family, friends, and the familiarity of their home. After taking some water and a handful of dried berries and nuts, each took their turn falling off to sleep.

At daybreak, Minty was awakened by the early morning chirping of hungry birds and squealing squirrels. As she roused to the sounds of Mother Nature, she reached over and shook her brothers awake. In a hoarse, sleepy voice, she urged them to make sure that the smoldering remains of the fire were snuffed out. While they finished up, she passed them enough hoecakes and water to satisfy their hunger. Araminta could tell that her brothers were still a little sluggish from the previous day's journey, but they could not linger there any longer. They had to move on. The young men followed their sister as she led them through the forest and along the creeks.

Several hours later, they saw a clearing in the distance. They were elated by the thought of freedom, and the three runaways quickened their pace. Soon, they began to race north toward the tobacco fields. Harry ran as fast as he could, but he found it hard to keep up with his older sister and brother. He tried to outrun them, when his foot became entangled in debris. He stumbled and landed on his arm. Pain shot through his hand and wrist. Araminta and Ben were alarmed by Harry's cries of pain. They were hoping that he was not seriously hurt, so that they could continue the escape. Concerned, Araminta took hold of her brother's hand and examined it. After careful inspection, she decided that it wasn't seriously injured. She ripped off a piece of her underskirt, soaked it in the nearby stream, and wrapped his hand to reduce the swelling.

"Brutha', it's time fo' us to move on," Minty said, lovingly placed her hand on his shoulder. The threesome started off once again toward the open clearing. Minty was hoping that they could get to the fields without any more problems.

By now, the overseer would've told Eliza Ann Brodess that Araminta, Ben Jr., and Harry had escaped. Grieving the loss of her husband, Edward, and dealing with her new responsibilities to manage a household of nine children, finances, land, and slaves had taken a mighty toll on her. She was mentally drained and physically exhausted. Eliza was aware that some of the slaves would run off, as was common when a master died. So it was no surprise to her to hear that the three had done just that. Eliza was going to do what was necessary to track them down. She had reward advertisements posted in Bucktown and Cambridge and negotiated with slave hunters.

Araminta, Ben, and Harry finally reached the open field. They could see a weathered barn just beyond it. In the distance, they could also see horses and cows grazing lazily. They needed to get to the barn as fast as they could without being seen. Minty knew that it would be the only safe place to hide until it became dark again. She worried about the possibilities of being seen, but she urged her brothers to run.

"Run fast as you kin. We needs to get to dat barn. Keep low. Now go."

Ben and Harry jolted forward and broke into a swift run across the field. Adrenalin kicked in at full throttle, as though they were flying. Their brogan-clad feet, although tired, carried them speedily in the direction of the old red barn. Neither of them said a word, but their thinking was the same. They needed to get to that barn as fast as they could to stay ahead of the patrollers. Slaves running through open fields, once caught, would be severely punished. Araminta ran alongside her brothers. Her legs were beating wildly against the inside of her underskirt. As they ran, gushes of air filled their open mouths and nostrils. Panting heavily, they knew they were only a few yards from the barn. Safety was within arms reach.

Feelings of relief were dashed when in the distance they heard the sounds of horses' hooves, wagon wheels, hounds barking, and the cries of several slave hunters. The hunters spied the moving dark figures in the field—telltale signs of runaways. The hound dogs, taking cues from their masters, knew that their prey was near. They snarled and yelped, as they ran alongside their masters. The white men knew their job well and took pleasure in catching niggers. It was just a matter of time before they would capture these Negroes, too. If these slaves were who the white men thought they were, Eliza Brodess would pay them well for their return.

Araminta and her brothers could not take the chance of getting holed up in the old barn. They knew that would be the first place the patrollers would look for them. Minty instructed Ben and Harry to run past the barn and off to the right into the next wooded area. Hopefully, they would find refuge there. The brothers quickly veered in that direction, while Minty managed to keep up with them. Although the three were in excellent shape and able bodied, they could not outrun the horses and hounds. They could see the wooded area up ahead. They yearned for the coolness of it, but within minutes yapping dogs and angry white men surrounded them. Knowing that their capture was imminent, they slowed down and stood still. Each hunter took his whip and lashed the three slaves to punish them severely for their transgression. Their clothes were ripped off to show bear skin. The worn leather cut deeply into their black backs. The lashes caused deep wounds; blood oozed freely. Araminta, Ben, and Harry cried out in excruciating pain and begged for mercy.

After beating them mercilessly and showing no remorse, the hunters tied their wrists and ankles with coarse rope. Laughing at the pain they had inflicted, the hunters viciously grabbed each runaway and shoved them onto the wagon. The slaves did not dare speak, but they searched sympathetically for each other's eyes as they were returned to the Brodess Plantation. The three knew that Missus Brodess would make an example out of them with more punishment to discourage other potential runaways. Even in silence the three knew that nothing would keep them from trying to escape again. In fact, they were now even more determined.

John Trevillion Stewart was a prominent shipbuilder on the Eastern
Shore of Maryland. Ben Ross, and at times, Harriet Tubman, worked
for him. Stewart was known to pay a fair wage to slaves. (This
historical image was provided by Stewart's descendant Robert
Stewart.)

CHAPTER TWENTY-TWO

—

Flight for Liberty

It was late fall in 1849. The sun had begun its slow descent on this autumn evening and was soon to vanish behind the tall poplar trees. Five-year-old Ann Marie was at the water pump a few yards away from her grandmother's cabin. The little girl's biscuit-colored skin was damp from playing all day. She was quite thirsty after having romped around with the other slave children. The cold well water trickled down her dry throat. She took some more. She knew it was about time for her aunt Minty to arrive. She always came on Saturdays for supper, and sometimes she would bring her husband, Uncle John. Ann Marie could smell the sweet aroma of her grandmother Rit's cooking, which was the telltale sign that all of her family would be there soon.

The young girl decided that she would meet her aunt as she came through the woods. She trudged off to the wooded area beyond the cabins and seated herself on a large tree stump to wait for their dinner guest. Some time had passed when she heard a deep voice calling softly to her. Startled because she didn't hear anybody approaching, she spun around in the direction of the voice. It was Aunt Araminta. That's the way it was with her. You never knew she was in your presence until you actually saw her. She walked lightly even in the woods. Anybody else would've been heard stepping on twigs, branches, and other debris crunching or crackling with each step, but it wasn't so with Araminta. A warm smile appeared on Ann Marie's face, and her dark brown eyes met Minty's. They softly hugged one another. Minty could not take her eyes off of the precocious child. Her heart swelled with love for the little one. She would never forget that horrendous day when the master had taken Ann Marie's mother, Sophe, away and sent her to a distant plantation. Araminta and the rest of the family took special care to make sure that Ann Marie felt loved in the absence of her mother. One might say that it was a blessing that the child had no memory of the pain that ripped through the family that day.

"How my punkin be?" asked Araminta.

"Good, Auntie. But why you be's so late?" Ann Marie responded.

Amused, Araminta quipped, "Nex' time I be's here early just fo' you."

Just as the two started off for the cabin, Araminta slumped to the ground and fell into a deep sleep. Normally a young child would have been frightened, but not Ann Marie. It was not the first time that she had seen this happen. Her grandparents warned her that whenever this happened to Minty, just leave her alone until she wakes up. Ann Marie knew that it would be some time before Minty would come to. So she decided to sit back down until Araminta awoke. The little girl sang a couple of her favorite songs to pass the time. Ann Marie noticed her aunt's eyes opening. She knew that this meant that everything would be all right. Slowly rising to her feet and realizing what had happened, again, Minty took Ann Marie's hand and walked to the cabin. By the time Ben arrived by wagon from the Thompson Plantation in Caroline County, Rit had just finished preparing a mouthwatering supper. As usual, the table was set with crocks and platters of collards, yams, crab cakes, ham hocks, chitterlings, and hoecakes. Ben motioned for his family to come together and bow their heads, while he blessed the food.

After blessing the supper, they all overfilled their plates, enjoyed their food, and talked about everything that had happened since their last visit. Reverend Samuel Green, a minister at Bazzel Church, also dropped by. (Rev. Samuel Green was a relative of Rittia, supposedly close, and a renowned abolitionist in his own right.) After they finished eating, Rev. Green asked the family to gather around the hearth, as he led them in singing their favorite spirituals. The family rocked and swayed. Their soprano and baritone voices rose in unison as they sang "Swing Low, Sweet Chariot."

Araminta was saddened by the thought that this was probably the last time she would be together with her family. She knew that she was to be sold and separated from her husband and loved ones, so she made the momentous decision to escape on her own. She knew that it would not be easy. She knew that she could be returned and punished again, but she was willing to take the risk. Araminta understood the cruelty dealt to slaves who were sold to the Deep South. If she was going to be separated from family anyway, she was determined to make her flight for liberty this very night. Minty was devastated that her husband had refused to join her, although she understood that he had no desire to escape. As a free black man, he did not want to be hunted down, punished brutally, and treated like a runaway slave. Tears filled her dark eyes, as she recognized that this was a bittersweet occasion.

Araminta knew that she could confide in her sister Mary Ann. She wanted to let her sister know about her plan to escape. Not wanting anyone in the family to suspect what she was up to, Araminta beckoned for Mary Ann to join her outside. The cool night air embraced them. It was late, and they sat fireside in the common area of slave row. Most of the slaves and the overseer had retired for the evening. The orange-red embers were slowly losing their warmth. The sisters sat awhile in silence. Minty wanted to make sure that no one was in hearing distance. Mary Ann was anxious that Minty was about to share something important. Araminta looked at her intently and leaned closer to reveal her scheme to runaway.

Under the starry dark sky, Minty spoke in a low voice. "Do ya' hears missus is gonna try ta' sell me off again?"

Mary Ann nodded in agreement. "Yez, I hears that. But it aint jus' you, Sistah. We hears that mos' of us to be sold. Probbly me too, 'fo too long."

"I needs to tell you that I goes tonight. I don't wants to leave, but don't wants to be sold either. I knows I am leaving my husband and my family, but if I don't goes I be a slave. If I run and don't gets caught, I can be's free."

Mary Ann understood her sister's decision. "Sistah, we's sho gonna miss ya'. Yous a brabe and good woman. Don't knows whut we's gonna do wif' out ya'. Ya' loves yo' family and ya' always be ready to hep us all. And you gib praise to the good Lawd ev'ry day."

"God be willin', wes all gonna be togetha' agin one day in da' free place they calls da' North."

"Dat sho' be nice, Sistah. Meb'be dat be's God's plan fo' us."

Araminta and Mary Ann stood and embraced.

"Now, dis be's our secrit. Cain't tell no body. Ya' know ya' cain't tell Mamma. Cain't says nuffin 'til afta' I goes. I's headin' out at minnight and ain't gonna be lookin' back."

The sisters walked, arm in arm, back to their mother's cabin. They went in and found their brother Henry teasing little Ann Marie and Samuel Green bidding farewell to their parents. Rit had worked so hard on the meal; Minty and Mary Ann cleared the table and washed the plates. It took them no time at all to finish. It was getting late. Sam, Mary Ann, and Minty needed to get back to their own cabins before they were considered missing. There was so much food left over that Rit encouraged them to take as much as they wanted with them. They carted off small portions of leftovers in bowls covered with cloth. Minty made sure that she took enough dried fruit, nuts, carrots, and snap peas for the long journey.

Before she got to the door, Rit caught sight of the bundle and said, "Girl, that food must been good, seems like you taking enough to last you a good while."

Araminta turned toward her mother, and with a faint smile said, "Night, Mamma."

As she stepped into the cool air, Araminta tightened her wrap and hummed "Steal Away." She headed for the woods, but turned for one last look. With teary eyes, she scanned the silhouette of the home and memories that she would leave behind. It was a vision that would be emblazoned in her mind forever. Now, she looked to the future to live life as a free woman.

Although saddened, Minty was extremely motivated to embark on the perilous journey. She would follow the same plan that she and her brothers used for their earlier unsuccessful escape attempt. They had almost made it to the Quaker woman's house before they were caught. This made Minty even more determined to make it this time. The Quaker woman was known to assist slaves on their trek to freedom. She would provide them with food, hide them, and direct them to the next stop on the Underground Railroad. Araminta, like most slaves, had heard stories about this railroad without trains. It was a network of sympathizers (mostly Quakers and abolitionists) who were dedicated to the cause of freeing slaves. Runaways had traveled the Underground Railroad for many years. This part of the trail extended from the Eastern Shore of Maryland, through Delaware, and Philadelphia, and on to Canada. Minty knew that if she could get to the Quaker woman, her flight for freedom would be much safer and easier. She also knew that she needed to overcome the obstacles that led to her previous capture and return to Eliza Brodess.

Araminta knew that she would be well ahead of the slave hunters by leaving at this late hour. With a vessel of water and a variety of bread, nuts, dried fruits, and raw vegetables, she began her travel on the familiar route. Trudging through the woods at night was frightening. Although her father had prepared her for the realities of nightlife, it was another thing to actually experience it. She could hardly see anything in front of her, except where streams of moonlight lit her way. She used her calloused hands to feel her way around thickets of trees, low branches, and brush. Her ankles were swollen from treading through hundreds of yards of woodland debris to make it to the first rest stop. While the smell of damp earth pierced her nostrils, Araminta could hear animal and insect noises in the distance. As she reached a small clearing, she spied an owl's luminous stare, as her eyes rested upon the gleaming moon.

Araminta decided to rest on a tree stump for a moment. Opening her satchel, she pulled out a handful of the nut-berry mix and washed it down with water. A simple rest was all she wanted before she continued her journey. As she sat there eating, her mind drifted to thoughts of freedom and what it would mean to her. She had never known freedom. She could only imagine, like thousands of other slaves, what this thing called freedom was all about. All she knew was that it had to be better than being taken away from her husband and family. She knew it had to be better than being treated like a farm animal. She knew that it had to be better than being denied the privilege to read and write. And she knew it had to be better than toiling for one white family for an entire lifetime. Minty was willing to risk leaving the known for the unknown, in the hopes that she would reach the North and find a life of liberty.

After she finished eating, she started the trek again. She was confident that she could make much headway, before the patrollers could pick up her trail. She continued on in the black of night, letting the North Star be her guide. Her father, Ben, told her that following the North Star and the Choptank River in the opposite direction would eventually lead her to Delaware. Although Delaware was not a free state, there were a number of abolitionists and Quakers who supported slaves seeking freedom.

As she gazed upon the North Star, Araminta felt content that she was that much closer to liberation. With only her face and hands exposed, layers of muslin and heavy cotton clothing covered her hair and body and shielded her from the relentless mosquito, swamp mite, and beetle bites. Her feet were protected by the toughness of thick-leathered brogans. Over the next few hours, she plodded her way through the expanse of timberlands. According to plan, Minty knew it would take roughly two days for her to complete the hazardous journey. The Quaker woman's house would be her safe haven and the light at the end of the tunnel, and getting there would be the beginning of her passage to Delaware.

Minty was extremely tired by now. In her weariness, she thought about how far she had come. She knew for sure that she had made her way beyond the Brodess, Meredith, and Hughes Plantations. Although she was secure in knowing that she was near the Quaker woman's house, the fear of being captured still lingered in the back of her mind. The slave hunters did not let moss grow underfoot. Certainly, someone had been hired to seize and return her to her mistress. The pursuit would be relentless. The thought of it caused her to maintain an acute level of awareness for every sight and sound that surrounded her. The mistress would be eager to get her back. Slaves were considered property, and if Araminta was not captured and returned, her owner would bear the loss of 250 dollars. Minty would have been worth much more had she not suffered the debilitating head injury.

Araminta's weariness and troubling thoughts did not deter her from moving forward. She decided at that moment to praise God for bringing her this far and asked him to continue to guide her on her mission. She remembered her father's words that the will of God would be done and that each one of us is here for a purpose. She hoped and prayed that the Lord's plan for her was to live as a free woman. With the thought of God leading the way, she was inspired to forge ahead with even more determination.

The sun had set twice on her journey. Again, Minty gazed upon a beautiful full moon and glistening stars. The North Star beamed in its usual location. She followed it, as it seemed to lie just ahead of the swamps. Tall grasses surrounded the still waters. She was cautious not to disturb the nightlife whose home she was encroaching upon. She walked as softly as she could. She treaded so softly that she could not be heard. All of a sudden, Minty thought her eyes were playing tricks on her. She rubbed her dry eyes to make them focus more clearly. Squinting, she thought she saw a flickering, yellow light in the distance. She was not absolutely certain, but she suspected that she had nearly arrived. Swiftly, yet quietly, she moved toward the light. Her heart pounded faster and faster as she approached the light. Minty was aware that Quakers and other sympathizers burned candles or oil lamps in their windows at night to signal runaways of a welcoming safe haven.

As she approached cautiously, the night sky illuminated a clapboard house with bluish-grey stone steps that led to a small veranda. Just as Araminta had hoped, she could now see a shining candle glowing in one of the front windows. Long lacy curtains draped its bright reflection. Araminta quietly walked around to the back of the house. A few yards away stood a carriage house and stables. She could not see the horses, but the smell of their presence lingered in the air. These surroundings were unfamiliar to her; however, she felt a sense of safety and comfort. This house was a place where she could relieve her weary body and please her growling stomach. She tapped on the back door. Anxious yet hopeful, she waited patiently for someone to answer. The door opened slowly, and a tall white woman with wheat-colored hair and deep-set blue eyes ushered Minty in.

"Who are you?" she asked the Negro woman.

"I's be a friend of a friend," Minty responded guardedly.

She was told to use these code words to alert a sympathizer that she was a runaway. However, if the person she was speaking to was not friendly to the cause, she could be in grave danger. Minty remembered the candle in the window and was convinced that this woman was a friend.

The white woman asked Araminta her name. She responded in a low voice.

"My name is Araminta. I am heading north. I hears you kin hep me."

"Yes, I am here to help you, friend. But you look tired now and must be hungry."

"I sho' is, ma'am."

The woman was a Quaker and did not reveal her name, but quickly went to the hearth to prepare food for the hungry runaway. Araminta was seated at a nearby table. Before long, the Quaker woman put a bowl of porridge and cornbread in front of her. The lady asked Minty if she would like some water. She nodded yes, while gobbling down the food.

"Where did you run away from?" the woman asked curiously.

Minty wiped her cold, dirty hand across her face.

"I is from the Brodess Plantation. The missus must have the slave catchers huntin' fo' me. I be gone more than two days now. I needs to move on to Pennsylvania. There, I bees free."

"My husband and I will do our best to help you get there. But now you need some rest. In the morning, my husband will carry you on to another friend in Delaware. Then he will help you get to Pennsylvania."

The white woman led Minty up the stairs to the attic. Minty

was surprised at what she saw. Three beds were neatly made and ready for visitors. The woman said that Araminta could sleep in the bed closest to the door. The lady lit a candle and set it on a small table beside the bed. She bid goodnight to Minty and slowly closed the door behind her. Minty could not believe what she was seeing, what she was hearing, and what she was feeling. She was overwhelmed by this extraordinary experience. Never before had a white person treated her with such respect and dignity. Minty felt like a real human being rather than chattel. She now knew that there were white people who would actually treat her as an equal. Araminta thanked God for this enormous blessing. She laid her exhausted body atop the straw-filled mattress and drifted off to sleep.

The morning sun filled the room. Minty awoke to a soft rapping on the attic door. A familiar voice spoke through it.

"Araminta, Araminta."

"Yes, missus. I's woke. I bees ready right quick."

Araminta stretched her body and crawled out of the comfortable bed. She rubbed her blurry eyes, took a deep breath, and walked over to a bowl and pitcher at the other end of the small room. The tepid water felt good against her chestnut-colored face. Her hands needed a good washing, too. She spent a few extra minutes to scrub off all the dirt that had accumulated over the past few days. On top of another table sat a clothes brush. She made long sweeping strokes against her clothing to release the buildup of dust and soil from the woodlands. Her brogans were next to the bed. She pulled them onto her feet and walked through the door.

Araminta descended a short flight of stairs and opened a door that led out to a long hallway. Curious, she looked around. In the daylight, she could see four small bedrooms and another flight of stairs. She took the stairs and found herself in a foyer. A candle and a Bible were placed upon a three-legged table that sat underneath a window overlooking the front lawn.

Minty began to feel somewhat out of place when she heard, "Come, Araminta. Let me take you to the kitchen. I was up early this morning and made some hominy, eggs, and crab cakes."

Araminta followed the tall woman into another area of the house. Sunlight filled the room from several six-paned windows. It was the closet thing to heaven that she had ever seen. One wall had a large cupboard filled with crocks, bowls, plates, cups, and platters. A roaring fire blazed inside the open hearth, and she could smell fresh bread baking. Near the back door was a round, wooden table with four chairs. She recalled the comfort she had felt while eating at that very same table some hours ago.

"Right after we eat, I will take thee to the carriage house where my husband will be waiting for you."

"That be's right fine wif' me, ma'am. I thanks ya' for all ya' doin' fo' me. Ain't no one evva' done nothin' like it befo'. I's real thankful."

"Araminta, you and I are God's children and now we are friends. I am helping you because God made all men and women free, whether black or white. No man has the right to overrule God."

"Yessum, I knows that be right. My daddy tole' us the same thin' many, many times. It bees good to hears ya' say the words."

"Praise the Lord," said the Quaker woman, who donned a sheer white bonnet tied neatly beneath her chin.

"Amen, good Lawd Jesus," Araminta whispered solemnly.

After saying grace, the women ate in silence. Both women cleared the table and washed dishes as soon as the meal was finished. Araminta could not remember ever standing side-by-side with a white woman for any reason, let alone washing dishes. A faint smile crossed her face. She began to think that this feeling must be something of what it was like to be free.

The Quaker woman and her husband did not believe in slavery. They had made a moral and religious commitment to do everything in their power to help eradicate it. It had been many years since they were first recruited as friends on the Underground Railroad. Many Quakers and abolitionists worked together as a collaboration of friends to feed, clothe, hide, support, and transport runaways. Their homes, barns, attics, and cellars held thousands of freedom seeking slaves over many years. They assisted runaways from as far as the Deep South to Pennsylvania.

Both husband and wife had lived through similar experiences in their original homeland of England. They believed in the Quaker religion and way of life, which was not tolerated there. They were not brutalized because of their skin color; though, they had endured ridicule and oppression because of their faith. Moving to America gave them hope of escaping the oppression and discrimination. Once they arrived here, the oppression centered on Negro slaves. Racism was rampant, systemic, and legal. They recognized the damage to the human spirit of everyone involved.

While Minty fantasized about her new freedom, the Quaker woman put her hand on her shoulder.

"I think you better go now. My husband is ready to take you on to the next stop. I wrapped some food for you and filled your water vessel. He is well-known for helping slaves to escape, and he takes them to the homes of other Quakers. Don't worry, he'll get you there safely."

"Yessum, he sounds like he be a good man. I be feelin' safe a'ready. Cain't beleebs I comes dis far. Now, I knows I kin make it. Thanks ya'. Thanks ya', Ma'am."

They walked outside to the back of the house. The Quaker woman spoke in soft tones.

"I don't want anyone to suspect that thee are a runaway. Take this pail of water to the front of the house. Water the flowers, vegetables, and herbs in the small garden. This way, anyone passing by will not think thee is on your way to freedom. They will think thee are working for me."

Araminta busied herself for a short while. The scent of Mother Nature's flowers caused her nose to tingle a bit. She loved the fragrance.

The Quaker woman called her to come to the back of the house. Handing Minty a piece of paper, the woman said, "Araminta, everything should be alright. Take this piece of paper and keep it close to you at all times."

Assuming, and rightfully so, that Araminta could not read, she told her what was on the note. The white woman said that the note had a man's name on it. She explained that the man was a friend of a friend and that he could be depended upon to assist any runaway. Araminta would never forget the sound of his name, William Still, and she would later learn that he was a free black man. She was told to produce the note when she arrived in Pennsylvania, and to ask anyone, black or white, to direct her to Mr. Still. Minty gratefully took the note and put it in a pocket deep within the fold of her skirt.

The Quaker woman's husband sauntered up to them. He

was a tall, thin man with broad shoulders and a long, silver beard. Dressed in overalls and a wide-brimmed hat, he approached Araminta.

"Morning, Araminta. My wife tells me you are ready to get on to the next stop. So, we are on our way to Delaware. It is not too far from here. Let me help you up into the back of the wagon."

He hid her behind a number of large sacks. With great appreciation, Araminta turned and exchanged goodbyes with the woman. She then hunched down behind bags of wheat, flour, and sugar, as the man covered her and the rest of the cargo with a large piece of canvas. The man embraced his wife, climbed up the side of the wagon, and settled down into its well-worn leather seat. He took up the reins and tapped the rear of the horse gently, asking it to move into a trot. The Quaker man assured Minty that although this would be an uncomfortable trip, she would get there safely.

"Don't worry, I have made this trip many a time with many a slave. In a few hours, we will arrive at Mr. Garrett's home. He's a good man, and he will help you the rest of the way to Pennsylvania."

The road was rather rough, but Araminta was glad to be riding rather than walking. She was grateful for the Quaker man's help, and she said loudly over the din of the wagon, "God bless ya'. I knows God will heps us to gets dere safe."

As she lay there in the back of the wagon, she crossed her arms in a comfortable position and felt a sense of comfort as she heard the horse's whinny. The man instructed her to remain covered no matter what. He told Araminta that he would let her know that they had arrived safely by saying, "Thee are among friends."

They were nearly at the end of their journey. Minty was not able to see the sun in order to tell the time of day, but she knew they have driven for several hours. She was exhausted, hungry, and thirsty. It was rather hot under the canvas. As sweat poured down her face, she fumbled for her water vessel and sack. She gulped down a good amount of tepid water and devoured a handful of nuts and berries. This would satisfy her for a while. Although hungry, the driver knew that they would soon arrive at their destination. He could see the familiar shape of the house as it stood off in the distance. He knew that Mrs. Garrett would offer them a good meal and a place to rest.

CHAPTER TWENTY-THREE

—

Free at Last, Thank God Almighty

M aking good time, the driver and the fugitive finally reached the Garrett property at 227 Shipley Street in Wilmington, Delaware. Thomas Garrett and his second wife, Rachel Mendinhall Garrett, were active members of the Quaker Society. Thomas was a descendant of a long line of Quakers who emigrated from England in the 1680s and settled in Pennsylvania. Rachel, too, came from a strong abolitionist, Quaker tradition. Growing up in the early 1800s, both learned to value human life, whether black or white, and to reject the evils of slavery. Each, in his and her own way, had helped hundreds of slaves seek freedom in Pennsylvania where slavery was illegal.

The Garretts eventually moved to Wilmington, where Thomas built a successful iron, coal, and steel business. There they continued their antislavery endeavors, and were well-admired by abolitionists along the Mason-Dixon Line for their assistance to runaway slaves. Their humanitarian efforts demonstrated their lifelong goal to help as many fugitives as possible. They sheltered Negroes in their home and also provided food, clothing, and money to help them make a new start in the free land. With the help and dedication of the merchant and his wife, the churning of the Underground Railroad dealt a decisive blow to the unrelenting institution of slavery.

Thomas began his personal crusade against slavery as a young man, when a free Negro servant was snatched from his home. The family was devastated when she was kidnapped, and they were to later learn that she was sold into bondage. Garrett was determined to locate the abductor, and he finally tracked him down at a navy yard near Philadelphia. From that time on, Thomas and his family were sympathetic to the cause and were driven to protect the lives of fugitive slaves. They spared no cost to bring their religious and political convictions to fruition.

The Garretts heard a driver pulling his wagon into the carriage house, which was attached to the rear of their home. Thomas and his wife waited for a familiar knock at the back door. The cryptic sound signaled the arrival of a runaway. Rachel moved swiftly to welcome the guests, while her husband followed in step. She opened the door to the carriage house and warmly welcomed the Quaker man. The driver retreated to the back of the wagon and carefully removed the canvas covering. The Quaker man held out his hand and helped Araminta to her feet.

"Thee are among friends," he said.

Araminta was relieved and overjoyed. Those caring words were music to her ears. She climbed out of the wagon and followed him over to Mrs. Garrett. The rather simple yet proper lady extended her hand to Minty and welcomed them.

"Welcome to our home. We have been expecting thee."

"I thanks you, Ma'am," said Araminta. The bearded driver introduced Araminta to the lady of the house.

"Mrs. Garrett, this is Araminta. Araminta Tubman is a runaway slave from the Brodess Plantation in Bucktown, Maryland."

"Right nice to meet ya', ma'am," Minty quickly responded.

"Well, Araminta, we are certainly glad to have thee here. We know thee have traveled long and hard to get here."

The woman pulled her husband forward gently by the arm and introduced him.

"Araminta, this is my dear husband, Thomas Garrett."

Thomas extended his firm hand to Araminta. She was not used to touching hands with whites, but she knew that this was a sign of friendship. Araminta took his hand and shook it rather timidly.

"How are thee, Araminta?"

"I is doing right fine, Suh."

"Well now, let me take us to the kitchen. I have a meal waiting for us. I think we could all use some sustenance."

The three followed the woman to a small but ample kitchen. The table was set for four. Each took their turn washing their hands at a nearby basin before sitting to eat. The table was full of food. The aroma of fresh-baked bread filled the air. Steamy root vegetables were plentiful. There was a platter full of oven-roasted chicken. One could see that there was more than enough food for the four of them. After Thomas said a blessing, the food was passed around for everyone to sample the delicious fare. There wasn't much talking at first, but the sounds of good eating could be heard. From the looks on their faces, the food was quite satisfying to the weary travelers.

Thomas asked Araminta about her escape. Minty was not used to talking in front of whites, but she felt she needed to oblige them. She shyly began to reveal the details of her escape.

"Well, Suh, it was awhile back when Missus Liza Brodus wants to sell me and my brudders Henry and Ben. She says she had to 'cuz her husband, Edward, die. She says she needed the money. So my kin and me sets out to run away. We almos' gets to the safe house where the Quaker woman be, but we gets caught by the 'trollers and hounds. They whupped us 'til the blood ran good. Dey chained us and we walks back to the Big House. The missus was not kindly to us when we got there. Sometime after, I decides to take off agin'. My husbin, John Tubman, a free Negro, don't wants to go. I leave him be and the rest of 'em. I do loves 'em all, but I don't wants to be sold. It was hard, real hard. But I gets to a Quaker woman's house. She and her husbin', here, brings me to ya', Suh."

"Well, Araminta, thee are safe here. Mrs. Garrett and I have welcomed many, many runaways in our home. There have been so many that I have lost count, but my wife says that there have been hundreds."

Araminta began to think about the hundreds of slaves that had traveled long and hard to reach this destination. She could not read or write, but she could imagine the number of people that had passed through this house. Each fugitive slave came with a name, a family, and a story. She knew now that these white people had to be inspired by God to put their lives, families, and homes in danger should they be caught hiding slaves. Deep feelings of gratitude swept over her.

Thomas turned to the man with the silver beard and thanked him for delivering Araminta to Wilmington safely. They passed a few more pleasantries before the driver indicated that he best be on his way back home. He did not want his wife to worry, and it would take several hours to return. Mrs. Garrett wrapped some chicken and bread in a wide piece of cloth for his ride back to Maryland. The Quaker man thanked his friends, bid his farewells, and left by way of the carriage house.

That evening Araminta, Thomas, and his wife, Rachel, sat and talked for hours about Minty's life on the Brodess Plantation. She spoke of her grandmother Modesty, her parents, her brothers and sisters, and her husband, John. Araminta shared the story about how she got the scar on her forehead and how she would sometimes fall asleep without notice because of it. She also recounted the failed escape with her brothers and how happy she was to be successful this time. Araminta told them about her enslaved family members' owners—the Greens, the Pattisons, Brodesses, and Thompsons—and she did not forget to tell them about her good family friend John Trevillion Stewart, who did what he could to help them escape. With all that, there wasn't much left to tell, and nightfall was fast approaching.

The threesome felt more acquainted now. Stories of generational slavery gave way to each bidding the other goodnight. Mrs. Garrett showed Araminta to a small room at the end of the long, narrow hallway. Araminta stepped into a clean and simple room. She untied her bandanna to show her crinkly, black hair. She removed her over clothes and stood near the bed dressed in quilts and pillows. Minty carefully placed her hair wrap and clothes on a wooden chair nearby. She wearily removed her brogans and set them by the foot of the bed. Completely exhausted, she placed her tired body atop the soft quilts and thanked God for the path of assistance that she had received. Once again, she found herself in the home of a white family, and she pondered how they freely accepted her as a guest. No words could describe her feelings. All she knew was that she felt enormous gratitude. Taking a deep breath and wiping tears from her tired eyes, she drifted off to sleep.

Dawn came quickly. Minty's soft-brown eyelids fluttered open, and she released a wide yawn, snuffing out the sound with the back of her hand. She stared at the ceiling for a moment or two, while she collected her thoughts and reckoned with where she was. Araminta was startled at first, but then she was embraced by a calming feeling. Without wasting another minute, she jumped out of bed and washed at the water basin.

Rachel Garrett was waiting to hear evidence of her guest awaking. She knocked lightly on the door. Araminta, not fully dressed, quickly piped up.

"Yes ma'am, I think I sleeps too long. I's comin'."

"Oh no, Araminta, that is fine. I bring thee some clean clothes. I think they should fit. Take them and wear what thee can. Meet with us down at the end of the hall when thee have finished dressing."

Opening the door, the woman passed Araminta a bundle of neatly stacked clothes. The bundle smelled like fresh air and sunshine. Minty placed the clothes on the bed and tried them on one by one. She was able to take a clean blouse of bleached muslin, a clean black bandana to tie around her hair, a dark woolen skirt, and a large woolen wrap to wear around her shoulders. Minty tidied up the room and left her old clothes in a neat pile on the floor. She left the room feeling clean and presentable. Although her brogans were still a little dusty, she planned to wipe them down outside. Araminta remembered to put the slip of paper with William Still's name on it in the pocket of her new skirt. She could not possibly forget the note from the other Quaker woman.

When she arrived at the doorway of the kitchen, she saw the Garretts seated and talking with a Negro. He was rather tall and slender, and he spoke in a clear, deep voice. The three of them turned as she approached.

"Good morning," they said in unison.

"Mawnin' to y'all, too," Araminta responded pleasantly.

Thomas and the Negro man stood up. Garrett warmly introduced them.

"Araminta Tubman, this is William Brinkley. He has agreed to take you on to Philadelphia. He will make sure that you get to free land and meet with William Still. Mr. Still is a very good friend. When you get to Pennsylvania, he will help you get settled there. Mr. Brinkley helps us with this part of the trip all of the time. He will be happy to take you on to Pennsylvania."

The black man extended his hand and said, "It's a pleasure to meet ya', Araminta. It won't be long before you are free. The Pennsylvania line is only 'bout twenty-five miles from here. In a few short hours, you will be a free woman."

Araminta heard the words, but she had a hard time grasping the reality of them. She didn't quite know what freedom meant, yet she knew she would do whatever was needed to get it. Now that reaching freedom was very near, she began to feel somewhat anxious. While the Garretts and Brinkley were obviously overjoyed, she was still trying to conjure what it would actually feel like to be free. She had no frame of reference, but Araminta felt satisfied that she would soon learn what it felt like.

They all sat and ate a light meal of biscuits, buttered hominy grits, and brewed tea. Minty's thoughts raced with memories of her husband and family. She smiled to herself thinking they would not believe what she was experiencing here. Shaking hands with white folks, holding long conversations with them, eating with them, and sleeping in their homes was foreign to most Negroes. It dawned on her in that very moment that this experience had to be something of what freedom was like. She had now realized that this feeling of calm, peace, and security was what she had longed for. The good Lord had answered her prayers. Before long, she would be totally free at last.

After the meal, Mrs. Garrett urged William and Araminta to move along. They needed to set out within the hour in order to make good time. Although Brinkley was a free Negro, a free Negro assisting a fugitive slave was in as much danger as a white person doing the same. William had made this trip hundreds of times before, but caution and good judgment were always needed. He set out to ready the horses and wagon for the journey ahead.

The Garretts walked Araminta outside. They stood at the entrance of the carriage house and waited for William to back out the wagon and horses. Minty didn't know exactly what to say. She knew her heart was full of thankfulness for these two people who she had come to know for such a short period. Saying thank you to them did not seem as though it would fully express her feelings. Araminta extended her hands to reach out and touch theirs.

She searched their eyes and finally said, "God bless y'all. Yous hepped me and all the otha' slabes. 'Cuz of you, we be findin' freedom. I neva' forgets you, neva'. I thanks the good Lawd for ya'."

"We know how you are feeling, Araminta," Mrs. Garrett confessed.

"Our thanks will be our knowing that you are free and no longer a slave," Thomas said.

The three of them held hands for a few moments. After lightly kicking the wagon wheel to release dust from her boots, the slave woman boarded the wagon. This was the beginning of a very long and endearing friendship for years to come.

Araminta and William drove off headed toward Pennsylvania. Along the way, they exchanged stories about their lives. Some of them were similar, while others were quite different. In between the stories, they sat quietly and took in the panoramic view of the countryside. They rode past a number of farms where cattle and sheep grazed lazily in the pastures. Wild horses ran free as the wind on acres of open land. They took in the sights of acre upon acre of crops needing to be harvested, stored, and hauled to market. Araminta's heart ached for the ones she left behind. On the one hand, she felt such happiness at the prospect of gaining freedom, but on the other hand, feelings of loss overwhelmed her. Tears of happiness and sadness filled her eyes in that bittersweet moment. The silence was welcomed.

In between the clopping of horses' hooves and slapping sounds of the reins, her thoughts jostled back and forth between her plantation home in Bucktown to her escape to the hospitality of the Quakers. Then her mind rested on the thought that freedom would soon be hers. A sense of serenity washed over her.

She reckoned that this would be as good a time as any to decide what name she would carry for the rest of her days. Most newly freed slaves took different names to elude slave catchers. It was kind of exciting to ponder the name she would take. She thought about it long and hard when a vision of her mother emerged. She reminisced about her mother's touch, her smile, and her feistiness. Rit was strong, compassionate, and a woman of God. Who better to name herself after than her own mother? The decision was made. Araminta would now call herself Harriet. The name felt right and natural. She whispered to herself, "My name be's Harriet. Harriet Tubman."

Brinkley turned and asked, "You say somethin'?"

The escaped slave shifted and looked into the driver's deep brown eyes and said, "My name be's Harriet. Harriet Tubman."

They gave each other that knowing smile. This marked the beginning of a new life for the woman named Harriet Tubman, who would later be known as the Moses of Her People.

It was not long after when William finally turned to her and said, "Harriet Tubman, you are now free as a bird. We just crossed the Delaware-Pennsylvania line. Now, you are a free Negro woman. Thank God another slave is freed."

Harriet heard the words, and for a moment, she felt lightheaded. She simply stared at William.

William looked at her and said, "Harriet, I said you are on free land. We are in Pennsylvania. You are a free woman."

Harriet lifted her dark hands to the open skies and whispered, "Thank ya', Jesus." She said it again, but this time a bit louder. "Thanks ya', Jesus."

Tears streamed endlessly down her round cheeks. She asked William to stop the wagon. Having seen this reaction so many times before, he pulled in on the reins and signaled the horses to stop. As they slowed, their deep brown hindquarters quivered before standing still. Harriet climbed down from the wagon. Her heart throbbed wildly in her chest. It pounded so strongly that she could hear the beating in her ears. The feeling of being free slowly invaded her entire body, soul, and spirit. There was an incredible wave of relief, peace of mind, and calmness that washed over her.

She got down on her hands and knees and kissed God's free earth. With her fingers, she scratched at the rich brown earth, until she was able to gather up enough to draw to her nose. The brownish-black soil smelled full of life. She lifted her head to the late day sun to feel its soothing warmth on her tear-stained face. She smiled at the yellow orb shining brightly overhead, and she shook her head, as if to say, I made it.

With the love and guidance of God Almighty, Harriet thought to herself, "I am free. Thank God Almighty, I am free at last." Rising slowly, she wept quietly as she thought about her husband, John, and her beloved family. Shaking, she made her way back to the wagon.

Thomas Garrett was a staunch supporter and friend of Harriet Tubman. Thomas Garrett funded Tubman's rescues and provided safe haven to hundreds of slaves traveling the Underground Railroad.

Part Four

—

FREEDOM

CHAPTER TWENTY-FOUR

—

Philadelphia

Harriet and William rode in silence. Neither one said a word as they privately took in the beauty of the countryside. The well-traveled dirt road was flanked by hundreds of trees. They stood majestically with their greenery swaying along with the light breeze. The travelers occasioned upon several clearings along the way. Before reaching each clearing, Harriet caught sight of the sun peeking through the thickness of tree limbs and foliage. She savored every minute, not knowing why she thought that the air seemed different. Could it be that the air was cleaner, sweeter, and thinner on free land?

Harriet filled her nostrils with the sweet freedom air as she tried to steady herself while the wagon jostled along the rough trail. The freedom seekers came upon a vista ahead that was as wide as the eye could see. Low-growing grasses now surrounded the path. With a quick rap of the reins, the horses snorted, dropped their heads, and then raised them high while giving way to a faster gait. The horizon in the distance began to become clearer.

Out of the expanse of low grasses rose a blurred yet defined semblance of a building in the distance. Before Harriet could speak, William said with an air of certainty, "There she is, Philadelphia, the city of freedom and brotherly love."

Overwhelmed and excited all at once, Harriet was filled with anticipation. She and William smiled at each other knowing that Harriet was at the crossroads of a new life as a free Negro woman. How that life would unfold could not be predicted. But one thing was certain, slavery and plantation life was now part of her past. Her future, although unknown, was welcomed with all of her being. Even the horses seemed to sense the newness and challenge of the moment. Their dark coats glistened under the late day sun as they majestically strode toward Harriet's new home.

William had successfully completed his task. He had delivered another grateful soul from the jaws of bondage to freedom in Philadelphia. Quite pleased with his accomplishment, he pulled back hard on the reins bringing the wagon and horses to a sound halt. The safety and security of her journey with William had ended. Harriet knew that it was now time for her to move on. Feelings of pride, achievement, and gratitude competed with those of sadness and separation from all that she held dear. It was indeed a bittersweet moment. Loneliness had already begun to creep into her heart. Not wanting to become overwhelmed by her thoughts and feelings, she made a deliberate decision to sort them out later.

Harriet clasped William's outstretched hand as he helped her step down from the wagon. She planted her brogans firmly on the cobblestone street. Her feet were slightly unsteady after the long trek. She tugged at her full-length muslin skirt to make sure that it was situated correctly. She did not bother to fix her hair; she knew that it was uncomely. She could not remember the last time she had put a comb through the thick, crinkly mass. She simply used both hands to smooth down the ends. She reminded herself to get a piece of material to wrap and cover her hair. A knowing smile appeared upon her lips as she thought of her mother and the other Negro slave women on the plantation with their hair tightly wrapped.

Harriet ran her hand along the right side of her skirt. As she did so, she felt a small bulge in her pocket. She dug into the slit that cradled the piece of folded paper. This precious piece of paper was given to her on the other side of freedom. In her mind's eye, she envisioned the Quaker woman instructing her to keep this folded square safe and to hand the paper to anyone once she reached Philadelphia. The Quaker woman was certain that someone would direct her to a friend of the Underground Railroad.

Harriet knew that the woman assumed that she, a runaway slave, could not read nor write. And of course, the white woman was correct in her assumption. Harriet remembered asking her mother years ago why slaves were not allowed to read and write. She clearly recalled her mother making a simple hand gesture, as if to dismiss her question as an absurd notion.

"Minty, don't waste yo' time thinkin bout thins that neva gone hap'en. You, me, an no uhtha Negroes round here ebber gone learn nothin' bout readin' or writin'. White folks makes sho of dat," Rit had said.

Her mother was right. There was no time to think about that now. But Harriet had heard through the grapevine, though, that free blacks could learn such skills.

"Kin you read?" she timidly asked William.

Knowing that this was a common question asked by slaves he escorted to freedom, William replied, "Yes, I reckon I can.

Why you ask?'"

"Well, a kindly Quaker woman heps me 'long the way. She gives me this here paper. She says a name on it. She says he a friend. He can heps me."

"I reckon she is talkin' about William Still. He's a good man. A good Negro man. He is free, ya' know. He heps the slabes crossin' over to free land."

William took the paper from Harriet, turned it right side up, and said, "Yep. It states his name right here all right. His office is right over yonder."

Before rushing off, Harriet took in the sites and sounds around her. She had never seen buildings so tall. From the looks of them, each one had many, many windows, which could only mean that there were many, many rooms, too. There were people everywhere. Men, women, blacks, and whites were busily going about their daily lives. She started to walk in the direction of the building that William Brinkley had pointed out, but turned slowly toward her escort.

"Willyum, God bless you. You a good man. Lawd knows you bring me safe and sound to freedom. I have no money, but Lawd knows I give ya' all my thanks. Thank ya' fo leadin me through. I will neva forgit ya'."

Brinkley gave her a big smile and a wave and pointed to the small building where she would find William Still's office. He assured his passenger that all would be fine now. William Still would arrange for her lodging and help her find work. Harriet strode quickly toward the building and climbed several stairs. At the top of a small landing, she turned to wave to Brinkley for the last time. Her heart sank. All she saw was the back of the man who had secured her freedom. She watched as he and the team of horses set off on their way back to Delaware.

Harriet lingered a few moments longer before entering the building. She let the sights and sounds of Philadelphia wash over her. She was struck by how different it was from Cambridge, the biggest city near her Maryland hometown. She was flooded with thoughts of home. She thought of her husband, John, and her parents.

She whispered, "Oh my Lawd. My John. He is there and I am here. I is free, but everybody I knows and loves ain't here with me."

A lump formed in her throat. She felt a sudden urge to scream, but she decided she best compose herself. Without further delay, she opened a large wooden door, which opened to a long and narrow hallway. There were several doors on either side of the entry. Not knowing which door led to Mr. Still's office, she decided to knock on the first door to her left. A man's voice firmly called out, "Come in."

Harriet slowly opened the hefty door. She peeked around the corner and her eyes fell upon a rather pleasant looking Negro gentleman seated at an oak desk. There were several ladder-backed chairs placed along one wall. Another small wooden chair was placed to the man's right. Reams of paper were stacked on a table across the room. Harriet felt shorter than her five-foot frame amidst all of the paper and furniture that filled the room.

"May I help you," the man asked politely.

"Sorry to botha' ya', Suh. My name is Harriet. Harriet Tubman. I bees lookin' fo' a Mistah Willyum Still."

Harriet's head and eyes lowered. Still recognized the familiar stance and lack of eye contact from someone experiencing freedom anew and chuckled heartily.

"I am William Still. Please take a seat, Harriet."

Harriet settled herself comfortably on the small chair nestled next to Still's desk.

"May I ask who sent you?" Still asked.

"Alls I know is she's a white Quaker woman. She writes ya' name on dis here papah. She says ya' a friend."

"That's right, Harriet. I am your friend. I am here to help you get settled in Philadelphia. You are now free. Philadelphia is free land. Welcome."

"Thank ya', Suh. Ah ben feelin free ebber since Willyum Brinkley and me come through the countryside some time back."

"I know that feeling. I am free now, but I was born a slave, along with my mother, father, and seventeen brothers and sisters. And it is my job as the head at the Vigilance Committee to help escaped slaves. My friends and I will help you get settled here."

Harriet's heart was bursting with gratitude. But the only words that she could seem to mutter were, "Thank ya,' Suh."

"You are most certainly welcome." Before Still could finish his sentence, he noticed that Harriet had slipped into a slumber. She was fast asleep. Her chin had dropped, and she appeared to be resting peacefully with her rough hands folded gently upon her lap.

While Harriet rested, Still made arrangements to get word to his friend J. Miller McKim, another member of the Vigilance Committee, that accommodations were needed by nightfall for one female runaway. Word soon came that one of McKim's Quaker friends had a place for Harriet. Still was pleased that everything was in place for the newest freedom seeker. Not much time had passed when Harriet roused. Her mouth was extremely dry. She didn't want to impose on Mr. Still, but she asked if she could have some water.

"Not only do I have water for you, but we have found a room for you," Still announced, while handing Harriet a cup of cold water. "Once you are settled in, you and I can have a talk about your escape. I will record all of the details about your journey and your family, with the hopes that you will reunite with them one day."

Just the thought of reuniting with her family and husband warmed her soul. "I likes dat very much," she said with great anticipation.

Harriet had made a new life for herself in Philadelphia. She resided on Pennsylvania Avenue, and she and William Still became fast friends. She would often drop by his office just to say hello. Even though she enjoyed her freedom, her heart and mind were never far from her family. Not a day passed that she did not think of them. She somehow felt closer to them knowing that Still kept track of all new freedom seekers. By now, she had told him her story. He knew about Master Brodess, her parents, and siblings. He knew how the family was devastated when Linah and Sophe were sold off. She told him about her tragic head injury, and she explained how she suffered from sudden sleeping seizures as a result of the horrendous blow. She was confident that if any of her family members were to reach Philadelphia, William would make sure that they would find each other. That gave her great comfort.

Harriet looked around her small living quarter. It may have been small, but she felt safe and comfortable. She finally replaced the tattered piece of muslin that hung over the single-paned window. She ran her nimble fingers across the bright white lace. The sun shining through made it seem even brighter. One of the women that she worked for in Cape May had gifted it to her. Harriet was appreciative of the cast offs, remnants, and trinkets given to her by employers. One of her possessions was a Bible she had received from a family in New Jersey. She kept it on top of a clothes chest in one corner of her room. She knew the word of God. She couldn't read the words, but having the book with her made her feel protected and secure.

Harriet didn't have much, however, she didn't need much. In the other corner of the room, there was an old table with a metal basin placed on top, which was usually filled with water for washing herself. Harriet remembered that the water was now two days old and would have to be replenished. On the wall opposite the door, there were five wooden hooks. There she hung several ankle-length skirts, bloomers, toppers, night clothes, and hair wraps. She kept a pair of brogans on the plank wood floor beneath her clothing.

There was not much to be done now, but to get ready for bed. Her bed was only big enough for one person, and that was fine with her. She would not want anyone but John sleeping next to her anyway. Her eyes swelled with tears at the thought of him. Her eyes smarted and her sinuses stung. She sniffed loudly while mucous trickled down the back of her throat. Somehow she knew she would never see her husband again, but she needed him. She wanted him. The loss of him made her nauseous. Harriet felt so alone as she crawled into bed. She was weakened by the very thought of him. She cried herself to sleep.

Morning came quickly. Harriet awoke groggy, and her last thoughts before drifting to sleep crowded her mind. She had to release those thoughts. It was time to get ready for work. It was hard labor, but she was no stranger to that. Working the tobacco fields and lumberyards was backbreaking work. Although she was considered sickly as a child, as a woman, she was known to have the strength of two men. It didn't take the backbone of two men to cook, clean, and launder for the white folks that she was employed by now—and she got paid to boot. The hours were long and the pay was meager, but it sustained her room and basic necessities. Harriet would work her fingers to the bone as long as she was free. Thoughts of John melted into the recesses of her mind. With her hair wrapped and fully dressed, Harriet left and made her way to do laundry for a Quaker family.

Harriet Tubman, Moses of Her People, was the greatest conductor of the Underground Railroad. She delivered scores of freedom seekers to safety and freedom in free states and St. Catharines, Ontario, Canada.

William Still inspired Harriet Tubman to become actively engaged in the Underground Railroad. He kept meticulous journal entries of escaped slaves, hoping to reunite them with freed family members. William Still held the positions of secretary and chairman of Philadelphia's General Vigilance Committee.

CHAPTER TWENTY-FIVE

—

Unrequited Love

T wo years quickly passed, and by now, Harriet was very familiar with the Philadelphia city life and Cape May. She had met so many people, white and Negro, who treated her kindly. She often found herself thanking God for her newfound freedom. Life was good. It still took her breath away to stroll past such sites as the Bishop White House, Pemberton House, Carpenter's Hall, and Old City Hall. She found the Liberty Bell to be the most impressive sight. To Harriet, there was no limit to God's goodness. Her breast swelled with pride when she caught sight of proud black men and women strutting their finery. It was an awesome sight to behold Negro women in tailor-made dresses and wide-brimmed hats that shielded their beautiful ebony faces and dark brown eyes from the glaring sun.

Even with the glory of God all around her, thoughts of John were never too far off. Harriet's heart sank as she tried to reconcile within herself how much she missed him. She loved her man. In her mind's eye, she could see the sweat pouring off of his reddish-brown face and him wiping his brow with the back of his rough hand. She looked with her eyes cast down just thinking about the deep dimples that appeared when he gave her that special smile. The dark mulatto (as they referred to him back home) was the only man she loved. The thought of another man touching her in a loving way made her skin crawl. Harriet rubbed her upper arms briskly trying to erase the goose bumps that prickled them. Her body and soul ached for him.

Thoughts of love and intimacy were suddenly gone, as sadder memories surged and flooded her mind. Harriet remembered just like it was yesterday, how John simply dismissed her ideas about running away from the Brodess Plantation. He did not want to hear another word about it. As she persisted, he became enraged and indignant. He put it to her quite plainly that he had no intention of going with her. Seeing him so angry was unsettling. John reminded her that he was a free man. He would not sacrifice life and limb for her or anyone. He would not leave Maryland. If she wanted to leave, so be it, but she would go alone. And of course, she did.

The sweetness of freedom did not squelch her need for him or remove the bittersweet memories. Harriet resolved to accept the good and the bad of life with her husband. That did not mean, however, that things could not change for them. She would no longer deny her irresistible urge to see him again. Harriet could not imagine that he did not miss her as much as she missed him. He would come with her this time, if she only had a chance to convince him how wonderful it was to be free on free soil. She would make him see that they would be happy together in Philadelphia. Harriet needed to return to Bucktown, and there was only one man she could entrust to help her.

Knowing that her friend William Still would be burning the midnight oil, Harriet decided to visit his office when she finished work at the hotel. She always enjoyed their visits, but most of all, she enjoyed him. He was always willing to stop what he was doing to chat with her. He was kind and willing to answer any questions. He was smart looking and well dressed. William often spoke about his work with the Vigilance Committee. He was passionate about abolishing slavery. He referred to himself and his friends who assisted runaway slaves as abolitionists. She was captivated, and she imagined herself working side-by-side with them. Harriet approached the office building and ascended the stairs. As usual, she entered the hallway and rapped lightly on his door. She recognized the familiar resonance of his voice and the shuffling of papers.

"Enter, please."

"Evenin', Willyum. Jus' passin' by. If you busy, I comes by agin' sometime."

"Oh, don't be silly, Harriet. I always have time for you. Take a seat," he said, pointing to the small chair alongside his desk.

"Willyum, I bin thinking mos' days 'bout my man, John. He got me wurred somethin' turble."

"I remember you said you left him behind. I recall you saying that he refused to escape because he was already a free man."

"Yup. I says it. But he don't mean it. He don't knows how it be's here. I will tell him 'bout da good here."

"It sounded like he already made his decision."

"I gots to goes back and git him."

After an awkward silence, Harriet finally said what needed to be said.

"Kin you hep me? Alls I needs is a litta' hep." She searched his eyes for approval.

"Harriet, I know you understand that going back to

Bucktown is very dangerous. On these trips in or out, people are jailed, maimed, or killed. If you are willing to take that risk for John, I can only say I will do what I can to help."

Harriet felt the flutter of butterflies within. Is it that simple? Ask and you shall receive?

Momentarily taken aback, she humbly said, "Thank ya', Willyum. Thank ya'. You's a good man."

"You are quite welcome. You know that my friends help with everything from food to clothing to transportation. I will contact friends from here to Cambridge to make arrangements for your journey."

As instructed, Harriet met William the following evening at his home. She approached the small clapboard house at 31 North Fifth Street. From a short distance away, she could see the amber glow of oil lamps in the front windows. She recognized the characteristic luminaries as a sign that marked William's home as a safe house. A calmness filled her spirit. Harriet knocked confidently on the front door. Although she had visited William and his family several times in the past, tonight would be different. By daybreak, she would not be cooking, cleaning, or laundering. Instead, she would be assisted by many good people to take a journey back into slave territory to be reunited with John. Reveries of their reunion were interrupted when William opened the door and welcomed her in.

William guided Harriet to the kitchen. The room was small, yet well-appointed with everything one would need to prepare meals. They both took seats at a sturdy pine table. Two large cups were already placed at each chair. William offered Harriet some tea and crusty bread with fruit marmalade. Harriet accepted his kind gesture. They chitchatted about the happenings of the day, but knew they had more important matters to discuss. An awkward silence befell the two of them.

Harriet waited for William to break the silence. She scanned the countenance of his face in anticipation of hearing about the plans for her pilgrimage to her birthplace. For a fleeting moment, she thought how ironic it was that her love for John drove her to revisit the slave land from which she risked her life to escape. Undaunted, she was resolved to be with him again. In his usual mellow voice, William revealed the plan.

"Harriet, this will not be a journey without its dangers. Enforcement of the Fugitive Slave Law is in full force. Our friends are being very careful about their activities on the Underground Railroad. Every plan for escape is treated with utmost deliberation and care."

Harriet was not sure she understood the meaning of his words, but she felt that William was going to help her.

"I have made contact with my good friend Passmore Williamson. She has assured me that everything is in place to put you on your way to Cambridge. Depending on the level of danger to you and our friends, you will move from safe house to safe house until you reach John's place."

With reserved excitement in her voice, Harriet managed to reply, "I's goin' to see my John agin. I thanks ya'. I thanks our friends. I thanks the Lawd. It ain't no easy way, but Lawd willin' I gets to John safe and soun."

"You will leave here for Wilmington. Your driver will come for you soon. The hour is late, so you need to get ready now. Eliza Brodess is unrelenting in her attempts to have you captured. You cannot return to Bucktown as a woman."

William left the kitchen and returned with an armful of

clothing. In the folded bundle, she saw what appeared to be a shirt, trousers, a short jacket, and a man's hat.

"Here, Harriet. Take these clothes and put them on. They may not fit well, but they will serve the purpose." William pointed in the direction of a nearby room.

Half giggling, even though it was a serious moment, Harriet took the bundle and strode quickly to the next room. She slowly removed her womanly attire and placed each piece neatly on the chair in the corner. Harriet returned to the kitchen dressed as a short, chestnut-colored man. Although ill-fitting, the clothes disguised her womanhood. William was satisfied. One hard knock followed by two short ones signaled that the driver was awaiting his passenger. William and Harriet bid each other farewell and expressed great hopes of seeing each other again.

The journey to Bucktown was long and hard. Not much had changed since she left her home and family a few short years ago. The agricultural economy of the South was rooted in the exploitation of enslaved free slave labor. Generations of Negroes, who rarely gained recompense for their back-breaking work, tilled the land and harvested sugar, cotton, rice, and tobacco. For most slaves, dreams of freedom were snuffed out by the reality that many who tried to escape were killed or maimed. Harriet had beaten the odds. She had escaped by the grace of God, and now, she was back again. Facing the threat of capture or death, she was determined to rescue her husband and return safely to Philadelphia.

Although a free Negro, John Tubman worked hard alongside slaves in the fields of Dorchester and Caroline counties. He took work in the lumber yards, tobacco fields, and shipyards. He was no stranger to the daily grind of arduous work. Like every black man in the South, he was destined to be a laborer. At the end of day, he longed for a hot meal and ached for the loving touch of his new wife, Caroline. Araminta was a distant memory. Though she was not totally forgotten. He still had a soft spot in his heart for that headstrong woman. He had told her not to go, but she left anyway, so he moved on, too.

Harriet knew just where to find him. In her mind's eye, she could see his comely face and hear his infectious chuckle. She felt the tenderness of his caress. She couldn't wait to see him face-to-face. She was a little apprehensive of what he would say when he saw her. What would he do? If the truth be told, Harriet was bracing herself for the surprise homecoming.

Harriet knew the area like the back of her hand. She decided not to walk in the open path leading to the cabin that she and John shared. Instead, she trudged through the tall grass surrounding the homestead. She removed her hat and stooped slightly so she wouldn't be detected as she made swift strides through the brownish-yellow green grasses. Even while wearing brogans, anyone walking through the open path would not have discerned her presence. Several yards outside of the cabin, Harriet slowed her pace. She crept lightly as she approached her husband's cabin. Harriet, dressed as a man, walked onto the plank wood porch. Hearing voices emanating from the inside, Harriet rapped steadily on the roughhewn door.

"Who dere?" John inquired.

"I's Minty. Open the doe', man. It's me, Minty."

"Minty, is dat you?" John asked, while opening the door furtively. He motioned for Caroline to stand behind him.

John opened the door slowly, then wider. The person

stepped in. He clearly recognized her voice, but the voice emanated from someone who looked like a man. Upon close inspection, John realized that the short chestnut-colored man standing in front of him was, in fact, Minty. He ushered her in.

Before Harriet could say anything else, she sensed awkwardness between them. It certainly was not the homecoming she expected. Moving closer to her husband, she saw a woman's face peek out from behind him. Harriet quickly stepped back. She was astounded. She searched John's eyes for an explanation. To avoid mistaking which woman he loved and was committed to, John pulled the other lady to his side.

"Minty, we wasn't spectin' nobody."

"I sees dat. Who dis here woman?"

"She be's my wife, Caroline. We gits together sometime back afta you leave dis place."

"I had to go. You knows dat. I neva forgets ya'. I comes to see ya' an tells ya' everthin' bout Phildelphia."

"Aw, woman. The time fo' talkin' is gone. Cain't be no me and you no mo'."

"Lemme talks to ya'. Cain't hurt nuffin. I gots a ho' lot to tells ya' bout."

"Caroline, go makes me some tea," John instructed. He opened the door and led Harriet to the porch.

"Woman, dere ain't nuffin to talks 'bout. You leave dis place. I gots Caroline now. I can't leave. I won't leave."

"I comes to see ya' cus ya' bin aching my heart an' bin on my mind fo' long time now. But I sees you's gon' an moved on."

"I's moved on. Yup. But I sho' is sorry you comes all dis way for nuffin."

"It werent fo' nuffin, John. My heart ain't changed. I jus'

ain't find whut I wanted."

John reached for her shoulder, but Harriet descended the steps swiftly. She could not look into those eyes again. She did not want to look into the face of the man who had betrayed their love. She also would not be further humiliated by having him see the flow of tears streaming down her face. Harriet was overwhelmed with feelings of hurt and loss. She was inconsolable. Pangs of sadness punctured her spirit.

It was well past dusk. Darkness had fallen all around her. She felt so alone, but darkness had its comforts. It shielded her. No one could see her in this pitiable state. As the tears continued to flow, she wiped them away with the back of her hands. Betrayal, humiliation, and heartache would befriend her as she walked down the lonely dirt roads to Cambridge. This place was no longer home to her.

CHAPTER TWENTY-SIX

—

Circle of Friends

I nstead of wallowing in the depths of loneliness, Harriet kept herself very busy. She wanted to fill every waking hour with enough work to keep her from dwelling on the past. It would not be easy, but it was time to move on. If that man did not want her, she certainly did not want him. She resigned herself to take in every bit of cleaning, cooking, and laundering that she could get her hands on—and there was more than enough work to keep her occupied. The days turned into weeks and the weeks became months. It seemed like the day would never come when the loneliness would be replaced by acceptance and peace of mind. But it did. It was not an easy road, and she struggled hard along the way. It was faith and forgiveness that got her through it. Harriet finally found the strength to reclaim her spirit and to recapture the joy of living as a free woman.

Not a week went by that she did not visit William Still. She thought he was a kind man, but more than that she admired the work he talked so much about. He often spoke about how much pleasure it gave him to help reunite families who had escaped from slavery. Harriet was also taken with the stories he told about the Underground Railroad. He talked about whites and free blacks, and how together they wanted to abolish slavery. He often mentioned words that she was unfamiliar with, like abolitionists, Methodists, Presbyterians, and suffragists, but somehow she understood that they were friends.

William told her that his friends lived everywhere from the Carolinas to Maryland to Philadelphia to Albany to Rochester, and further north to Canada and every place in between. They provided food, clothing, safe havens, transportation, and money to aid those seeking freedom. His stories were peppered with names that were now familiar to her. The likes of Thomas Garrett, Lloyd Garrison, Frederick Douglass, Gerrit Smith, and Eliza Wigham were mentioned. Harriet was inspired to know that so many people were willing to risk their own safety, security, and freedom to stamp out what they believed to be the unjust and immoral economic system of slavery. It was a risky business with dangerous consequences, yet the friends were relentless on their quest to dismantle the practice of enslaving human beings. Harriet grew more and more passionate about the abolition of slavery, and she was determined to find a way to serve the cause and her people.

Still was the keeper of information regarding the newly freed slaves who were directed to his office. Like Harriet, hundreds of runaways told their stories to William. Their testimonies revealed the burdens of plantation life. The newcomers reported their names, the names of their slave owners, and the plantations where they were enslaved. They gave the names of relatives and friends in the hopes of being reunited with them one day. Many free blacks shed the names given to them in slavery. Their new names and the location of their new homes were also documented. As President of the

Vigilance Committee, Still's goal was not only to assist families in finding each other after escaping, but also to help them either settle in Philadelphia or move farther north. He relied heavily on his friends in the movement to supply goods and financial support to aid in the transition from slave life to freedom and self-reliance.

It was late afternoon on a cool autumn day. William was in his office re-writing the testimonies of new runaways from Virginia. He had just finished the final version of the text when he heard someone knock at the door. Before answering, he took the writings and placed them in a secret compartment built beneath the desk drawer. One could never be too careful. Although it was free territory, Philadelphia was not off limits to bounty hunters and agents for slave owners. William kept the testimonies hidden to reduce any chances that they would be stolen and force countless numbers of slaves back into slavery.

Quietly, he closed and locked the drawer and instructed the caller to enter.

"Good afternoon, Sir. How can I be of service to you?" William asked politely.

"Well, Suh. I's John Bowley. I works at the shipyards in Baltimo'. I ain't had no wheres else to go. My wife and children ready to be sold off from the Brodess Plantation down dere in Mareland."

"Who is the plantation owner and exactly where is the plantation located?"

"It's in Dorchester County, Mareland. The mistress name is 'Liza Brodess. She done gone mad. Sellin' off all the salves. Her husband dead. Peoples say she needs the money to upkeep the house and the children."

William recognized the anger and anguish in the man's

voice. "Now don't fret, John. I believe we can help you. My friends and I know folks who can assist us. Who directed you here to me?"

"A white man. Name's James T. Stewart. He a shipbuilder near Cambridge. He gets me to da Chezzapeak. Then I meets up with a free black man. William Brinkley. He gits me here."

William dabbed his pen into the inkwell and transcribed the man's story. John told him about his wife, Kessiah, and their two small children Araminta and James Alfred. He stressed that they could be sold any day now. John explained that he had offered to buy his wife and children, but Eliza Brodess was asking a great sum. It was much more than he had managed to save from his meager wages. His only desire was to rescue his family.

Still finished what he was writing, and the two sat for quite a while discussing how the rescue would be carried out. William informed John that there would be a series of coded messages that would be sent to stationmasters along the Underground Railroad. Each one would wait his arrival, and then usher him, as quickly as possible, back to Cambridge. There, a friend who would help him abscond with his family would assist him. They would be brought through Baltimore and finally cross over into Philadelphia, barring any unforeseen catastrophes. Both men knew that a return to the land below the Mason-Dixon Line could be as fraught with danger as escaping from slave territory. The passage and enforcement of the Fugitive Slave Law made these journeys even more perilous. John decided that he and his family would take this risk. They would seek freedom rather than endure the heartbreaking separation.

Harriet arrived at William's office building. She looked up

to the window. She saw the silhouette of the oil lamp. It was not burning for it was not yet dusk. As she ascended the steps, she tidied the wrap around her hair. There was not much she could do with the smell of smoke in her clothes that came from the wood burning ovens used at the hotel. She softly rapped on the office door. She heard men's voices inside. Harriet knocked again. Studying the transom overhead, she waited longer than usual to be asked to enter.

"Come in," she heard William say cautiously.

Harriet cracked the door, peered into the room and saw William shaking the hand of a man whose face she could not see. She entered.

"Oh, Harriet, it's you. I am just finishing up here with a friend. John, you will need a room for the night. I will take care of that. We will meet in the morning to discuss the matter further."

"I thanks you, Mistah Still. Cain't tell you how much."

"Harriet, we do not have much time to visit this evening." William motioned the caller toward the door. The tall man turned to leave. His hat partially shadowed his face, but Harriet would know that face anywhere.

"John! John Bowley. Dat you?"

John was stymied. This woman's voice was so familiar to him.

"Could it be true? Minty, dat you? Ain't seen you in some time."

Harriet chimed in, "That sho' is true. Ya know they calls me Harriet now."

Without hesitation, the two strode quickly to each other. They clung to each other in a brotherly and sisterly embrace. Slowly, they released their loving hold, each savoring the warmth of family affection.

"How my niece and her babies be? The chilren must be ole' nuf to tend the gardins."

"Harriet, Kessiah, an' the chilren be real fine. But we gots some trubba. The ole missus seem like she gone mad. She be tryin' to sell off all the slabes. Kessiah and the children be nex."

"What's ya' fixin to do?"

"Dats why I comes to see Mistah Still. We talks. I believes he gonna heps us. I needs to git my family away from the Brodess place."

William Still was overjoyed to witness the reunion. This is what made it all worthwhile. He couldn't get a word in edgewise. Harriet and her niece's husband rambled on about all that was going on in Bucktown. He talked about the missus. He assured Harriet that her mother, father, brothers, and sister were well, but he made it clear in no uncertain terms that the threat of family separation was imminent.

"I goes back to git my John. He finds hisself another woman. Cain't say I likes it, but I lives widdit. 'Spect my mamma and daddy knows I bin back dere by now."

"Yez. We all hears you bin down near Bucktown. We's glad you comes and goes an' not gets caught. We hears you free, an' we thanks the Lawd for dat."

"I gonna goes back agin'. Dis time you and me bof' gonna bring Kessiah and the chilren out. Willyum, I knows you and John bin planning. I's ready to hep any ways I kin."

Silence penetrated the small office. William nodded in agreement. The spirit of freedom engulfed them. The time was ripe for another rescue. From Philadelphia to Cambridge and back to Philadelphia, coded messages would be sent out and stationmasters would be alerted. John and Harriet would execute the plan to rescue a young mother and her children from the jaws of slavery. Every effort would be made to ensure that Kessiah and her babies would escape the fate handed to Kessiah's mother, Linah. To her dying day, Linah was denied the love and affection of her children and her husband, Harkless Jolly. Harriet Tubman knew she, John and William had God on their side. The Bowley family would be spared this immoral injustice. Harriet and her niece's husband set out on their freedom-seeking journey by nightfall the next evening. Not only would the Bowley family be safe, but also Harriet made a vow to herself that she would use the network of friends and the Underground Railroad to free all of her family. With great success, John arrived in Cambridge.

John Bowley knew he had to act swiftly, yet without any undue attention being drawn to him. As he looked into the auction block, from a short distance away, he saw many people he recognized, especially John Brodess, the son of Eliza. He was there on behalf of his mother to ensure that the sale of Kessiah and the children was transacted. It appeared that the young white man was confident about himself and the auction process. The bidding was underway. The experienced auctioneer enticed bidders by exclaiming the great physical attributes, work capability, and child-birthing expectations of each slave showcased. The white men hung onto every word. The bidding was lively and purposeful. The slave owners or their agents were engaged in the speculative business of getting the best value for their dollar.

Kessiah and her children were next in line to be gawked at by all in attendance. James Alfred and Araminta squealed while being posted up on the auction block. Kessiah, a handsome black woman, held their tiny hands. She was frightened at the prospect of being sold. She quivered from head to toe, knowing that her new master would acquire her and the children at the highest bid. John made his way to the front of the assembly. It was not unusual for family members to purchase their enslaved relatives. He and his wife made eye contact. Kessiah became very nervous. She was not sure what her husband was going to say or do. The children motioned forward, catching a glimpse of their daddy in the crowd. Kessiah pulled them tighter to her.

"We've got a bid of $500 for this negress. The deal is that much sweeter with her two children. Do I hear $525?" A planter from Virginia cried out. But a white man from Carolina County quickly shouted, "$575!"

The crowd roared, and this signaled that this was certain to be the final bid.

John Bowley stepped forward and shouted, "$600."

The men in the throng grumbled; not one wanted to bid higher. The auctioneer was certain that another man in that crowd would outbid the black man.

"Do I hear $625? You know you will have a fine, hard-working negress with a bonus of two children. She's good for at least another ten children. Farm or plantation will be well set."

The planters assembled pondered over what could have been a decent acquisition. With a number of other slaves to be considered, there was a collective decision to let the bid stand.

"Hearing no other bid, I will accept $600 from that man," the auctioneer said, pointing at John Bowley.

Kessiah, Araminta, and James Alfred were escorted away from the auction block and led to the rear of the courthouse to join the rest of the purchased slaves. An auction attendant accompanied the mother and her children, and shoved them into the huddled mass of blackness. They all awaited their new masters or handlers to cart them off to work unfamiliar fields. Each slave fully understood that they might be sold again and again and again. They knew for sure that the blackness of their skin was an insignia of servitude. There was no escape from their birthright.

Before John finalized the sale, he scurried to the rear of the courthouse. As planned, he absconded with his family into the nearby marshland. By the time the auctioneer, the crowd, and the purchased slaves realized what had happened, the free black man had fled with his family.

"Keep low. Keep low," John commanded in a quiet voice.

"John, I's scurred to def. Where you takin' us? Da man be right behinds us befo' long," Kessiah expressed.

"Don't you neva mind. We got peoples waitin' on us down the way. Iffin' the Lawd be wif us, we be's dere fo' long."

Their greatest worry now was keeping the children quiet. John had not thought to bring the special herb to make them sleepy. The parents carried them against their chests. They decided to tell them a story to soothe them. The children listened intently. John told his babies that the jostling around due to their hurried gait was like riding a horse. The children liked that idea. The parents had to deceive the children, as danger was all around. Quickly, John took possession of a small boat waiting for them in the nearby inlet of the Choptank River. With his family secure, John took hold of the oars and propelled the vessel toward Baltimore. There, Harriet and her friends awaited them in a safe house. Harriet's heart swelled with love and pride as she reached out to her niece Kessiah.

She scooped up both children and brought them to her breast, as she kissed each one lovingly. She felt a sense of relief that she and family had been reunited. Harriet and her family made their way to freedom in Philadelphia with the help of their abolitionist friends.

CHAPTER TWENTY-SEVEN

—

Canada Beacons

Harriet looked around her living quarters. She had finally replaced the tattered piece of muslin that she had placed over the half window. She lazily walked over to the window and ran her dark fingers across the bright white lace. As she turned around, there was a large metal basin sitting upon an old wooden table in the corner of the room. She remembered the water in the basin was now three days old and would have to be dumped and refilled. There were five iron hooks along one wall where she hung her ankle-length skirts, toppers, wraps, sleep clothes, and washing clothes. She kept a single pair of brogans under the clothes on top of an old dusty rug that she found in the dark, damp alley between the buildings where she roomed. There wasn't much to do now, but to get ready for bed. Her bed was only big enough for one person, and that was fine with her. She would not have anybody, but John sleep next to her anyway.

Harriet's eyes filled with tears and smarted at the thought of him. Her sinuses stung as her nose began to run. She sniffled loudly as the warm mucus ran down the back of her throat. Harriet knew that she would never see her husband again. She needed, she wanted him. The thought of him caressing and loving Caroline made her sick inside. She felt so alone and abandoned. She lay down gingerly on her bed, as if weakened, and cried herself to sleep.

Harriet woke groggy, and she slowly remembered her last thoughts before drifting off to sleep. She would have to release those troubled thoughts, while she dressed and got ready for work. Now clad in a dark woolen skirt, long-sleeved muslin blouse, and underskirt, she quickly stuffed her stocking covered feet into her old, tattered pair of brogans. She left the room, locked the door, and headed off to launder and iron clothes for one of the families that she worked for. Thoughts of John melted into the recesses of her mind, as she made the hour-long trek to her paying job.

Working from dawn to dust without any breaks was grueling as usual. Harriet was being paid, so the employer expected a full day's work. She would leave in the evening with her hands raw and cracked from washing clothes with lye soap, but even with blistered hands, Harriet felt that having this pain as a free person was well worth the discomfort.

As she rounded the street corner, she saw a bright light glowing from the window of William Still's office. She knew that he often spent late hours writing entries in his logs on runaway slaves who had escaped from plantation life to Philadelphia. Harriet approached the building, walked up the steps, walked through the heavy wooden doors, and walked quietly down the hall. She rapped lightly on the door. William's deep, throaty voice beckoned her to enter. Harriet stepped into the office and found William sitting at his desk with reams of paper stacked high on either side. Sitting there, he seemed to be engulfed by the white, papery columns.

He looked up and said with a hint of weariness, "Is that you Harriet?"

"Yez, Willyum. I sees your light and knows you here workin' late ta night."

"Well, I'll be leaving for home soon, but I did want to finish this entry on the slave family who arrived today from North Carolina."

"Thanks the Lawd for ya'. Hepin' folks to fine places to stay and to work. I knows they is glad to see ya'."

"Well, yes, I love my work. It makes me feel good to know that more and more people like you and me have escaped the clutches of the savage beast of slavery. It is with great pride that I chronicle who the slaves are, where they come from, where they are going, and a little bit about their life stories. This helps immensely when former slave families and relatives want to find each other. It all gives me such great pleasure."

Harriet looked deeply into his tired brown eyes and knew that her visit would be short. She bid him goodnight and headed toward the door. Before she had completely stepped into the hall, Still called out to her.

"Harriet, you have been on my mind lately. I'd like you to come back tomorrow. There is something I'd like to talk to you about, but it will keep until tomorrow."

"I's will bees here right round da same time. You knows the folks I works for wants me to work to early evenin'. But I's be here directly after my work."

Harriet left the office and headed to her room. She was trying to recall the tone of William's voice. She wondered what he would talk to her about. Was it good news or bad news? No matter how many times she played his last words in her mind, she could not predict one way or the other. She simply said to herself, "Yes, Willyum. It will keeps 'til tomorrow."

Harriet returned the next evening to see William. She was more than happy to sit awhile with him. This always made her day. She enjoyed listening to his clear deep, voice recounting the challenges or triumphs of his day. To her, William was the epitome of a free black man. He was well-spoken, well-dressed, and worked very hard to make differences in the lives of Negroes. Harriet was honored to be a friend.

"Come in, Harriet. Good to see you. How was your day?"

"Ain't nuffin' happin' different from mose the otha ones. Jus the regla' cleanin', washin', an' totin'. But I's glad to do it knowin' I makes enuf to keeps me a rufe ova ma head."

"Harriet, how long would you say that you have been here in Philadelphia?"

"I's reckon bout two yeahs now. Mebbe little mo'. Good Lawd, man. I hopes ya' wrote me up like yo does all the res' of dah runaways. I wants to be found, too, iffin' my family comes lookin'."

"Don't worry, Harriet. I have written your story in my book. I can get to it in a jiffy if any of your folks come looking for you. And you're right—I met you right here in this office just about two years ago. It seems like it was only yesterday."

"Yez, Willyum. It do. It shorely do," Harriet said thinking back to that wondrous day.

"Back then, we knew that once you got settled here with some work and a place to stay, you would be here for quite a long while."

"Yep, I gots me some work, gots me a place, and I neva bin hungry yet."

"Well that's why I needed to speak to you today. I believe you have done well here. I've heard from the families that you work for that there's nothing you won't do to make their lives a little easier. And the people at the hotel don't know what they would do without you."

"I's glad they like my work. My momma always tole me dat if you work yo hardest an' it be the best, white folks will always need ya'."

"I can agree with that, Harriet, and the Lord knows you are not a stranger to hard work. But, I think very soon, you are going to have to do the hardest work you have ever done."

"I ain't scared of no hard work. You must gots somefin' big for me to do."

"It's quite big, Harriet. Do you remember our talk awhile back about the Fugitive Slave Law?"

"I reckon I does. You tole me dat da gov'ment gots a law dat lets massahs take runaways back to da plantashun. The massahs pays lotta money to git us back."

"That's right. There have been so many runaways now that the slave catchers are all over Philadelphia. They are looking everywhere for Negroes without free papers. When they find the runaways, they shackle them and cart them back to the South in wagons. Today, my friends reported that two wagons were loaded for the South."

A wave of insecurity briefly overwhelmed Harriet. She immediately recognized that she had not felt that feeling in quite a long time. It was unsettling. Harriet looked up to meet Williams' eyes. She was not sure what she would find in them. Once their eyes locked, Harriet could see that her friend was worried.

"What ya' hab to tells me, Willyum?"

"Harriet, after thinking long and hard about this, I truly believe that you need to make arrangements to move further north. The Fugitive Slave Law is being widely enforced. Slave catchers are not only here in great numbers—they are penetrating further into Pennsylvania and New York. More and more, free Negroes are being captured and returned as slaves."

"Willyum, you tellin' me I gots to lebe dis place. Dis place where my heart be, where my place be, where you be? Oh, Lawd. Pleeeez says dis ain't so. Lebe dis place, Lawd? Willyum, you says I goes furtha north?"

Harriet did not shed a tear, but she cried within. She had made a home for herself here. She enjoyed walking freely to and fro. She didn't mind the hard work. In fact, she had put some money aside to buy a white lace collar she wanted to wear to church on Sundays. She pictured the faces of everyone who was kind to her—the man at the bakery, the freckled man at the general store, and even the cobbler who had re-stitched her brogans at least three times. Of course, there was the little old white lady in the sky-blue shawl who would nod and wave to Harriet from her front porch as Harriet passed by on her way to work each morning. And she would certainly miss seeing the free Negroes dressed in their finery and walking with their heads held high. Without a doubt, she would terribly miss William; she loved him like a brother. Harriet looked forward to hearing runaways' stories and about the work of the Vigilance Committee. But she wondered if all of this was to be no more?

William could see that the young woman in front of him looked perplexed. His heart went out to her, knowing that the idea of moving further north was totally unexpected and perhaps unwelcomed.

"Harriet, I can imagine what you are thinking and feeling. I would not make such a suggestion unless I believed that your life could possibly be in grave danger if you remained here."

"Willyum, I knows you only does what is good for us Negroes. I knows that ya' means no harm. I reckon ain't nuffin' to cry ova. The Lawd is good an bin good. Ain't nuffin' to cry ova. Ain't nuffin wrong wit letting him take charge agin. I's ready."

William was quickly reminded how Harriet could adjust to the reality of given situations. She was not one to become immobilized when times got tough. She had often told him that she had complete faith that the good Lord would provide for her and was her source of strength. Hoping that Harriet would agree with the idea, William had already contacted several abolitionist friends to begin making arrangements for her.

"Harriet, you know that this kind of travel is long and hard. This time you will be traveling for many more days, even weeks. Arrangements will be made to accommodate you as you make your way north. The furthest north one can go. It's so far north that it is located beyond America. But when you get there, there will be no chance for the slave catchers to capture you. You will be in another country. It's called Canada."

"It sounds like dat will be right fine. Jus memba, keeps my story up, so iffin' my peoples eva come dis way you lettem knows wheres I be — Kan-na-da."

"In fact, the city is called St. Catharines. If all goes as well as expected, before long you will make your new home there. When you arrive, you will be welcomed by free blacks who will help you get settled. Harriet, Canada has opened its arms to the Negro. The taste of freedom is everywhere. Negroes own homes and businesses. The work is hard and the weather can be frigid, but our people have made a good life there. A free life. You'll never have to worry about being a slave again."

"Iffin' freedom be at dah end of dah road, I be right happy to be dere. The Lawd willin', I gets to Kan-na-da befo' long."

The two stared at each other. They knew their time together was very short. The moment was bittersweet. Already they knew that the heaviness on their hearts would linger for some time to come. The Underground Railroad connection was made, and friends of the underground operation were in place. The trek would be very long and hard and involve several modes of transportation from Pennsylvania through upstate New York to Niagara Falls, and onward to St. Catharines, Canada. Harriet was pleased to hear that she would not be the only fugitive slave on the journey. Eleven others who were also freedom seekers would join her. Courageous and caring free blacks and whites cautiously led Harriet and the other slaves from one safe haven to the next. Some risked their own lives should they be caught assisting slaves, while others would be publicly ridiculed and fined large sums of money.

They were all extremely dedicated to the cause. The freedom travelers were fully aware that their journey could end abruptly with being captured, but the reward of freedom was worth that risk. Many days after they left Philadelphia by horse and wagon, Harriet and her fellow fugitives were housed throughout New York State in Albany and Rochester. Friends of the Underground Railroad ensured their successful flight from slavery to freedom. After a short stay in Rochester, the freedom seekers would arrive at their destination. Reaching the country of Canada, the freedom seekers believed they had been delivered to the Promised Land. While in Rochester, the fugitive slaves were provided a safe haven in the home of the illustrious orator and abolitionist Frederick Douglass. Years later, Douglass eloquently described Harriet Tubman as the most courageous of abolitionists, because she consistently risked her own life to bring Negroes out of slavery to their birthright of human rights and individual freedom. By then, they had developed a fond and respectful relationship because of their unique roles on the road.

Harriet and the other freedom seekers were ushered on through Buffalo. They were about to have the most incredible experience of a lifetime. Slavery was a hard condition that many slaves could not escape, yet Harriet and the others walked across the suspension bridge from America into Canada and from slavery to freedom. It was surreal and real all at the same time. Harriet could barely contain herself. As she stepped onto Canadian soil, she knew what the rest of the refugees were feeling. She had had this feeling only once before. It was the same emotion she had when she first crossed over into Chester, Pennsylvania. It was that feeling of having an extreme burden lifted from one's shoulders. A merry spirit replaced her heavy heart. She didn't become giddy, but rather tearfully grateful. With the help and guidance of many friends on the road, she and the others escaped capture and the clutches of human bondage. At the same time, she envisioned so many others that had traveled part of their journey through the waterways, from the ports along the Eastern Seaboard, including the Inner Harbor of Baltimore, Maryland, and Mystic, Connecticut, to the Finger Lakes of New York to St. Catharines, Canada. Over the years, thousands of former slaves made their home in St. Catharines, Chatham, and Nova Scotia. These cities were about as far away as you could get from the Mason-Dixon Line.

A network of friends received them in Canada. St.
Catharines had become a mecca for escaped slaves. Many
Negroes already living there were the descendants of escaped
slaves known as Black Loyalists. The Black Loyalists (white
Americans were known as United Empire Loyalists) fought
side-by-side with Canadians who were loyal to Britain. They
fought for the British in the American Revolution and the War
of 1812. Many other blacks sought resettlement there after the
abolition of slavery in Britain and Canada. The British
Canadians vowed to give blacks their freedom in exchange for
their loyalty. They made good on that promise. With that
freedom came the opportunity to be self-supporting. They
could own land and sell their produce, poultry, and meats.
Later on, there were greater opportunities with the building
and operation of the Welland Canal. Businesses grew and jobs
were created. Employment could be found in mills,
lumberyards, shipyards, and factories. Other African
Canadians worked as skilled tradesmen: masons, coopers,
barbers, and carpenters. Also, there was a growing tourist trade
with the recognition that the waters of the springs had
healthful properties. Hotels were built to accommodate what
were mostly American tourists. Blacks found jobs as janitors,
chambermaids, groundskeepers, and cooks.

Shortly after their arrival, Harriet and the others had places
to live and work. As in most cities, the black community in St.
Catharines lived in close proximity to each other. Harriet lived
on North Street and attended the Salem Chapel British
Methodist Episcopal (BME) Church on Geneva Street. (Her
brothers and parents eventually lived with her here for a short
time after she rescued them.) In order to keep a roof over her
head and to provide for those who lived with her, Harriet took

work as a cook, laundress, and housekeeper. Her greatest work, though, was as an abolitionist. With help from her friends at the Refugee Slaves' Friends Society, Frederick Douglass, Thomas Garrett, and William Still, Harriet answered her calling to do God's work. She believed that Providence gave her the knowing that she was under his will to bring slaves out of slavery to freedom in the Promised Land.

Most of Harriet's rescues began with her leaving her North Street home. The grapevine was a reliable source of information, as was the postal system. The most famous Conductor of the Underground Railroad heard that her brothers were ready to take their journey to freedom. Without hesitation, the Moses of Her People, assisted by friends of the road, made her way from the Land of the British Lion's Paw back to the territory below the Mason-Dixon Line. Back in her hometown of Bucktown, Maryland, she found her brothers, Benjamin, Robert, and Henry, awaiting her arrival. The family knew the other two brothers, Harry and Moses, had already escaped.

The men knew of their sister's success in being liberated and her phenomenal ability to rescue other bondsmen from the jaws of slavery and deliver them to Canada. Although their journey was fraught with danger, Harriet ushered her brothers and three others to Philadelphia on the first leg of the journey and St. Catharines, Canada, on the second. Freedom was theirs, as it was for tens of others who Harriet had rescued. Returning to Canada after each rescue, Harriet knew more than ever how much she loved living there. Yes, Canada saw its share of problems between the races, but its laws also prohibited enslaving human beings. There, blacks, as free people, had a chance at working and living independently with dignity. Once no longer enslaved, the Ross men changed their names like most former slaves did. Benjamin took the name of James; Robert took the name of John; and Henry took the name Levin first, and then settled on William Henry. Each of them took the last name of Stewart, after their good master John Trevillion Stewart who was known to be an abolitionist. All Rosses who reached freedom in Canada, and eventually in Auburn, New York, assumed the last name of Stewart.

With the urging of her brothers, Harriet decided that it was time to go rescue their niece Ann Marie Ross. She was a young girl of marriageable age still living with her grandparents Rit and Ben. Wouldn't it be wonderful for her to join them in Canada? With her great beauty, she would surely find a free black man in Canada to marry and raise a family with. Harriet's brother Benjamin—or James Stewart—took in the newly rescued Ann Marie once Harriet delivered her to St. Catharines. Ann Marie—or Martha Stewart—lived with her uncle James and his wife, Catherine Stewart (whose former slave name was Jane Kane) until his death. After her uncle's death, Martha, Catherine, and Catherine's children, Hester and Elijah, moved to Auburn, New York. There they resided with Harriet Tubman on South Street Road for a time. And here is where Martha (now back to Ann Marie) married Thomas Elliot of the Dover Eight.

Three years after she rescued her brothers, Harriet made a frantic return to Maryland to free her aging parents. She heard that her father was in danger of being jailed for harboring Thomas Elliott and seven others who had escaped from Caroline County, Maryland. Thomas and the others made an incredible escape from Caroline County, only to be betrayed and captured in Dover, Delaware. Time was of the essence.

When she reached her parents' cabin (bequeathed to her father by his master, Anthony Thompson), they were grateful and excited to see her. Yet, Harriet sensed their trepidation. They were long in years and a little long in the tooth. Could they make the journey to freedom? Was it worth leaving their land and cabin, which fewer blacks could boast about? Dorchester and Caroline Counties were the only places where they had ever lived. Gently, but convincingly, Harriet let them know that separation or her father's death was not an option. Although her parents had both been given their freedom, it was time to escape the long hand of the law. All that was left was trust in their daughter that she would deliver them to a place where they would be safe, secure, and fearless.

Harriet's mission was accomplished. With the help of her friends, Rit and Ben, the parents of the Moses of Her People, reached Philadelphia. Harriet was proud to introduce them to her good friend William Still. As was custom, they gave him an account of their slave lives. Still put pen to paper and recorded their slave story.

Harriet made her last journey to Maryland in December 1860, just months before the start of the Civil War.

CHAPTER TWENTY-EIGHT

—

A Call to Arms

The War between the States, more commonly known as the American Civil War, was at best a war of contradictions. Just before dawn on April 12, 1861, Confederate forces opened fire at Fort Sumter, South Carolina. The people of the United States were thrust into a conflict of enormous proportion. It all seemed so reminiscent of the fervor during the Revolutionary War. Then, Americans were facing off with Britain to preserve life, liberty, and the pursuit of happiness. Now, in a flourishing nineteenth century America, Americans faced off against each other for these same values. Conflicting political and philosophical views spiraled into an explosive confrontation, and the war began.

Everyone had a life and death stake in the war. They were driven to protecting and preserving life, as they knew it or life as they wished it to be. The slave economy was at the core of the debate between those that supported it and those who opposed it. Americans were forced to take sides in a political battle that divided the North from the South, Republicans from Democrats, free state proponents from slave state protectionists, whites from Negro slaves, and abolitionists from slave owners.

The divisiveness had long been brewing, but came to a head at the election of Abraham Lincoln as president of the United States. His ascension to the presidency was deeply troubling to southern Democrats. Lincoln and his fellow Republicans espoused antislavery and supported legislation to restrict slavery to the southern states and opposed its expansion to the western territories. Their position on these matters, forced southern Democrats to support South Carolina and other states to withdraw from the Union. These states combined their forces to create the Confederate States of America under the leadership of their president, Jefferson Davis. Unbelievably, the two Americas were at war.

The battle raged on with the Union and the Confederates claiming victory at strategic fronts and ports. The armies on both sides suffered tremendous losses. Thousands of soldiers clad in either blue or gray could not escape the ferocious gunfire of the enemy. Not long into the war both Lincoln and Davis had to reckon with the reality that their military forces were significantly reduced due to death, illness, and defection.

Amid his many advisors, Lincoln reluctantly decided to bolster his forces by organizing and utilizing colored troops. Negroes from the North and the South were drawn into the war, each one hoping for liberty, not only for himself, but also for his brother and his people. The colored regiments were proud and fought hard to preserve the Union. They believed that a victory for the Union was a victory for liberty. Former slaves and free Negroes volunteered to the Union Army to help abolish slavery and create America where they would finally be free from bondage. Their troops also suffered numerous loses of life and limb, but they fought equally for the cause.

Abraham Lincoln did not regret his decision to enlist the

help of Negroes to join the Union Army. Under the direction of his Secretary of State William H. Seward, several of his most noble military elite—like Montgomery, Hunter, and Sherman—were responsible for organizing and leading Negro troops into battle.

Well into the second year of the Civil War, Seward convinced President Lincoln to call upon Harriet Tubman from his hometown of Auburn, New York, to join the Union forces as a spy, scout, and nurse. He didn't make this recommendation lightly. Seward was well aware of Harriet's exploits as an abolitionist. She had rescued scores of slaves from bondage. She had successfully secreted these slaves from the Eastern Shore of Maryland through Pennsylvania to Canada. Her confidence, fearlessness, and courage made her an excellent candidate to assist the Union in freeing and recruiting slaves. Seward had known her well; his good friend Frederick Douglass introduced him to her years before the war. Seward and his wife, Frances, assisted Harriet during her slave rescues by harboring the fugitives on the way to Canada in their kitchen and outdoor woodshed.

In 1862, the Lincoln Administration by way of Massachusetts Governor John A. Andrew sent word to Harriet Tubman in Auburn, New York, of their desire to have her join the War Department of the South. Harriet's life would take an interesting turn into a different kind of battle. A military battle was taking place in the South. Harriet was being called to travel below the Mason-Dixon Line. The Union Army and the Negroes in South Carolina were calling for her one-of-a-kind skill and determination to fight for freedom.

The crowing of roosters and chickens housed in the coops at her home on South Street Road on the Fleming-Auburn line awakened Harriet. The year was 1862. She awoke every morning knowing that she was blessed to have a home that she owned. A few years prior, her good friend (and then senator) William Seward sold her the property. She could walk out to her yard on the seven acres of land that she owned and gaze upon the geese that bantered about squawking and dipping their beaks into the dark earth. She also loved to smell the blossoms and see fruit hanging delicately from the many apple and peach trees. And of course, the chickens strutted lazily around the grounds or sat in the barn laying large brown eggs. God was good. Her land was good. Her home was good.

Harriet lived with her aging parents, her brothers, and several other boarders. Rit, her mother, suffered from the usual ailments of people her age, yet she didn't miss a beat making breakfast for her husband, adult children, and the others most mornings. Rit was up before the roosters this morning making fixins for biscuits, salt pork, and hominy for the hungry brood. She didn't mind having to wake up early. She savored the freedom to awake when she chose to. At her age, being able to cook for her family and the boarders was a pleasant chore.

Harriet arose from a welcomed sleep. She washed and dressed before joining her parents in the kitchen. As she descended a steep flight of stairs to the lower level, her nostrils were filled with the aroma of her favorite breakfast foods. The smell wafted throughout the house.

"Mawnin', Mamma. Mawnin', Daddy."

"Mawnin' to you, too," Rit and Ben said in unison."

"Sure smells good, Mamma," Harriet said as she sat herself on one of the ladder-backed chairs.

"We say that every morning don't we?" chuckled Ben. He

and Harriet shared a morning giggle. Rit ignored them, but appreciated their liking for her cooking. She loved cooking for her family.

"You goin' to the Pomroys today, Daddy?" Harriet mumbled between bites of her buttered biscuit.

"Yes, I goes there today. If there be 'nough time, I goes to the Fitches, too. They both needs work done in the gardens. Where ya' goin' today?"

Harriet replied in her usual straightforward tone. "This mawnin' I goes to the Seward mansion. Not early though. Miss Frances don't need me til late mawnin'. She's goin' to the orphanage to visit the chil'rens."

Ben, Rit, and Harriet said a prayer of thanksgiving before eating the hearty food set before them. All that could be heard was lips smacking. The gloss of sweet butter glistened on their dark, full lips. Finishing up their meal, they sat quietly for a few minutes thinking about the chores that lay ahead of them.

Overhead, they heard creaking of the floorboards as the others rustled about getting ready for the day. Harriet's brothers and boarders descended upon them and took their places at the old, sturdy pine table. Rit, Ben, and Harriet pushed away from the table and made way for the others to be fed. Rit moved slowly to the stove, returning with a pot of hominy to fill their bowls. Morning voices rose and fell into a loud muffled pitch. One voice could not be distinguished from the other.

A loud rap on the front door silenced the household. The rapping grew into pounding. Someone was determined to get their attention. Swiftly, Harriet made her way to the door. Before opening it, she called out to the person on the other side. "Who's there?"

"I have a letter here. It's a government letter addressed to a Mrs. Harriet Tubman."

Harriet felt the heaviness of the door while she jostled the brass knob open. It finally opened toward her, and she could see a rather official looking man standing on the stoop. In her hand, he held a large greenish brown envelope. Without hesitation, the slight gentleman spoke in a clear voice, "Are you Harriet Tubman?"

Harriet deliberately made eye contact with the white man and said, "Yes, Sir. I is Harriet Tubman."

The man handed her the envelope, and then asked her to sign her name on another piece of paper. With a sense of pride, Harriet lifted the pen and placed her X upon it. The man looked at her, and then looked at her mark. Without so much as a "thank you," he turned on his heel and left the premises. Harriet watched as he climbed up into his wagon. With one yank of the reins, the horses sped away.

Harriet quietly closed the door. She held the envelope tightly in her hand. Looking down at the telltale dark spots, she knew the marks were words. She also knew that another person would have to tell her what the spots meant. She never learned how to read or write. Ain't that something to reckon, she thought. What a shame Harriet couldn't read her own letters, especially one as important as this one. When Harriet returned to the kitchen, she told the others about the letter. They wondered why she would receive a letter from the government. She thought long and hard about it, too.

Harriet took the trek north to the Seward mansion at 33 South Street. Along the way, she admired the huge expanse of farmland. She loved being able to walk freely wherever she chose. Freedom was never far from her mind. Today, she was not in a hurry. She took the time to appreciate the scenery. She saw dozens of dairy cows mooing at the new grasses. Horses galloped playfully in the fields. The chickens and geese roamed freely around their owners' properties. Being close to the land was all she knew. Suddenly, her thoughts were flooded with memories of the Brodess Plantation. How different it was here. Negroes owned their own property, and she was one of them. God was good. She lowered her head in complete gratitude.

Harriet glanced toward the Quill farm where she saw several young boys running and screaming. She could not quite figure out what the commotion was all about. Then she shook with laughter. One of the lads was running frantically after a chicken. Harriet couldn't believe her eyes. The boy was trying to catch a chicken whose head was dangling alongside its body. The chicken didn't know which way it was going. But it was going fast, blood splattering everywhere.

When she composed herself, Harriet chastised the boy. "Aye, Boy! Let that there chicken go. With his head half cut, you let him go til he pass out. Leave him be."

"I thought I cut it clear through, but I didn't. My mamma is goin' to beat me for sure," cried the blond-haired boy.

"Well, let that be a lesson for you. Now, go an find your momma and tell her what you done."

The boy walked away sulking. He did not mean for the chicken to be in pain. He caught up with his brothers, not wanting to tell his mother what had happened.

Harriet continued down South Street. Just past Cornell Street, she enjoyed gazing at all of the beautiful mansions— one right after the other. The homes had so many windows, she was glad she didn't have to clean them. She had often done small jobs for many of the families there. The Hislops, Osbornes, Emersons, Pomeroys, and the Swifts treated her kindly and paid her well. They all knew that Harriet used her money to support her family and to finance her freedom ventures.

After reaching the Seward home, Harriet walked along the path leading to the side entrance. Seeing the small black woman approaching, Frances Seward opened the door. She greeted Harriet in her usual friendly manner. But before Harriet could speak, Frances rattled off a litany of things that needed to be tidied up or cleaned. She walked through the hallway toward the main living room while she spoke. Harriet's mind was not on cleaning. She would do that later. Right now, she wanted to know what the letter said.

She pulled the folded envelope out of a pocket in her full-length skirt. She politely waited for Mrs. Seward to finish speaking. Harriet broke in quickly, "Miss Frances, kin you read me dis letter? It comes today. The man said it was a gov'ment letter."

Frances turned slowly, as if awestruck. She carefully took the letter from Harriet's rough hands. She glanced at the front and back of the envelope. Frances finally spoke. "Harriet, this letter is from the Governor of Massachusetts. That is Governor John A. Andrew. It says that he is requesting your assistance in the Department of the South to work in military actions against the Confederate States. He goes on to say that you are needed in South Carolina. You will report to General David Hunter. They expect your arrival in the next few weeks."

Harriet bowled over. Almost at a loss for words, she inquired, "Miss Frances, is that letter telling me to help the Union in this Civil War?"

Frances was taken aback as well and gave her answer careful thought before responding. "Yes, it's very clear that that is exactly what is being asked of you, Harriet," she said.

Both women looked at each other in wonderment. Without a word, they knew what the other was thinking. This would be Harriet's most heroic and courageous undertaking. Frances motioned for Harriet to follow her into the kitchen. Each took a seat at the small round table. Frances discussed with Harriet the news she had recently heard from her husband, Secretary of State William H. Seward.

"You know Harriet, William has written me of late. He said that President Lincoln has decided to allow Negro troops to join the Union forces in the war against the Confederates."

"We's all been wondering what took him so long. Now, I will be down there right along with them," Harriet declared.

"The Union forces need you, Harriet. They know of your stamina, determination, and skills you developed conducting your rescues. You can now use them to help save the Union."

Harriet boasted, "I knows how to get slaves from one place to the other, and I nebba loss one yet, and need be, I will use my gun."

"So it sounds like you have made up your mind to go south again," Frances said.

"Yep. Nothin' and no one can stops me now. With the Lawd's hep, I will see the glory of vic'try. My peoples will be free," Harriet said confidently.

Harriet arrived at Hilton Head, South Carolina, ready for the rigors of war. She was met by one of the officers and was taken to the army campsite on the outskirts of town. She was carted by horse and wagon to where the troops were camped out. As they drove into the wooded area, the officer described to Harriet the kind of work that was expected of her. He impressed on her the extreme need for her to nurse and care for the sick and wounded soldiers. He was not shy about telling her that the Department of the South also needed her to perform intelligence operations to spy on the Confederates and scout out strategic posts where Union troops could infiltrate and ambush the enemy. The Union depended on her ability to come back with information that would be used for offensive attacks, raids, and destruction of Confederate properties, businesses, and strongholds.

Arriving just before dusk, Harriet witnessed what seemed like hundreds of Negro men in blue uniforms that branded them as protectors of the Union. The air was heavy with humidity and the odor of dried blood and dirty clothing clung to her nostrils. The men were in different stages of undress. Some staggered and limped around in blood-stained bandages wrapped around chest, leg, and arm wounds. Others stretched out on straw-filled mats moaning in delirium from more serious health problems. Still others, their faces drawn from exhaustion and hunger, glared at her as an unwelcomed guest.

Within a few short weeks, the troops grew to accept her presence and depended on Harriet Tubman. She carefully nursed their wounds and cooked their food. It was hard to find a soldier that did not love her delicious gingerbread cakes. She was often found making barrels of root beer to quench their thirst and soothe their dry throats. Harriet wasted no time in making sure that she helped to make the soldiers comfortable in any way she could. The goal was to keep them healthy and ready to fight for the nation and their lives. There was no mistaking that this was war. Harriet did witness many Negro soldiers take their last breath right there in Hilton Head, far away from their plantation homes in the South and homes above the Mason-Dixon Line. Freedom was at stake. Yet illness, disease, and death took their tolls on the once robust. They ravaged young men who fought for life, liberty, and justice under the party of Abraham Lincoln.

Although saddened by the serious conditions and watching the men clinging to life before passing over, Harriet was not disillusioned. Her faith in God—as the only force that could bring justice out of the war—kept her steadfast in her desire to see her people free. Harriet had an inner knowing that God would lead her people out of the land of Egypt and into the land of freedom. She was certain of that.

Harriet was up before dawn most mornings to make her way to the army hospital in Hilton Head. There she would greet the men in her special way, and in a soothing manner, she tried to bolster their spirits enough to get them through the day. One summer morning, she was struck by the moaning of a particular young lad. He could not have been more than fifteen years of age.

"Boy, I hears you groanin' suppin' awfil, son. Lets me git some cole wata' to wash ya' down," Harriet said.

"I ain't moaning cuz I's hurtin'. I's moanin' for my momma," the young man said. "Whens I lef' her, she wailed like nobody's bizness. I tole her I be back. But now, I don't knows."

Harriet said righteously, "God takes care all dat! We's just do the bes' we kin. He gonna keeps ya' or take ya'. What eva' way, you gonna be in the bes' hands."

Harriet left him momentarily to fetch more water and clean cloths. The young boy stared at the ceiling. Tears streamed down his dark cheekbones. Before Harriet returned, he fell into a slumber, while picturing his weeping mother standing near the rice field on the Carolina plantation.

Harriet returned to change the young man's bandages. She inspected his wounds. Although there were signs of healing, yellow-green pus oozed from the bloody wound. She cleansed the wound and applied a poultice of healing herbs. Holding the poultice gently in place with steady pressure, Harriet felt compelled to sing one of her favorite songs to him. In her contralto voice, she softly sang, "Swing Low, Sweet Chariot, Comin' forth to carry ya' home, Swing Low, Sweet Chariot, Comin' forth to carry ya' home."

Many former slaves were recruited by the Union Army to fight in the Civil War. Pictured here is Company E, 4th United States Colored Infantry. During the Civil War, Harriet Tubman served as not only a scout and spy, but as a nurse, as well, in Hilton Head, South Carolina.

CHAPTER TWENTY-NINE

—

Swan Song

Harriet walked a little slower these days. Her northbound stroll down South Street Road toward the center of Auburn was something she did less and less. Some of the young black men in the area who drove horse and wagons would offer Harriet rides. One young man in particular named Clarence Morgan Stokes, stopped regularly to take Harriet into town to shop, to sell her vegetables, or to visit some of the wealthy whites in the area. She enjoyed her rides with Bobby. He was of medium height, but had a very strong build. His deep brown skin looked as smooth as silk and glistened in the midday sun. She never did, but she had always wanted to stroke the glossy black curls that were closely cropped atop his head. She remembered him fondly, as she strolled toward home.

Up ahead, Harriet could see the familiar brick house that everyone knew as Aunt Harriet's place. It wouldn't be long now before she would reach the house and saunter along the path facing south and make her way to the side porch. As she reached the property, she had just enough energy to climb the steps and sit in her porch swing. It sure felt good to rest her aching bones. The swing was somewhat worn and rickety, but she was in her comfort zone. Only hard rain or snow kept her from spending time each day on that porch. It was there that she would sit and swing, sometimes for hours. As she swung back and forth, the swing squeaked. The squeaking sound had a pacifying quality about it.

Harriet Tubman Davis had lived in this house for more than fifty years. If the walls of the two-story brick structure could talk, they would tell of the lives and the deaths they had witnessed. They would tell of the frequent visitors from Harriet's friends and family. They would talk about the discussions that they heard about life's lessons learned, bondage, freedom, dreams deferred, and dreams granted. The walls would boast of giddy children playing in the meadows or sticking their tongues out to catch newly falling snow flakes or teasing the chickens and geese that strutted about the grounds. The walls would be remiss if they didn't mention how the old folks sat back after a long day, and reminisced about the old times and leaving slavery behind.

Harriet smiled to herself, took a long, deep breath and closed her eyes. Her grey-white hair was wrapped tightly in a dark kerchief. She rested her head against the back rung of the swing. Slowly, a vision of Nelson appeared. He stood there tall, straight-backed, and strong. His large, squared hands were hidden in the pockets of his overalls. His tattered hat was tipped slightly over his right eye. Plumes of smoke rose from the cigar he held between his full lips. Harriet could still smell the fragrant aroma of the tobacco burning. She didn't care for the scent at first, but as time went on, she learned to make friends with it. Now, she missed him and his ever-fragrant cigars.

Her second husband, Nelson Davis, was a Civil War

veteran. As an escaped slave, he enrolled as a soldier with the G8 U.S. Infantry serving with the colored troops. He and his comrades-in-arms fought against the Confederates in the bloodiest war ever on the soil of the homeland. Political principles and ideologies, the economies of the warring states, and the institution of slavery were the accelerants fueling the war. Negro men, like Nelson, were proud to join the Union Army and fight against the southern states that were bound and determined to cling to an economy that created wealth for whites from the back-breaking work of generations of Negro slaves. Thousands of men, black and white, lost their lives. Nelson and so many others escaped the clutches of the Angel of Death. Hundreds of other soldiers were left maimed or ravaged by illness and disease. It was during the war when Nelson first laid eyes upon Harriet Tubman.

She remembered telling her husband that she had no time for getting interested in no man during the war. She had her hands full keeping up with the sick and dying and scouting out enemy territory. That is when Nelson would tell her that that is exactly when he fell in love with her. He had never seen a woman, black or white, take command the way she did in every situation. He could not fathom how a woman half his size demanded attention and action on her explicit orders, and the men obeyed. She gave compassionate nursing care to those who did not know her name. Yet, they looked into her dark brown eyes searching for a chance at wellness. She baked ginger cakes and sold them to supplement the meager rations she was given during her service to her country. She and nearly eight hundred black soldiers, under the command of Colonels Montgomery and Sherman, struck terror in the hearts of the Confederates. During her scouting and spying expeditions, Harriet Tubman located commissary stores, ammunition storage areas, cotton warehouses, and stately mansions that were destroyed by the Union Army, leaving the South devastated and war torn. Amid the destruction, hundreds of slaves were freed and thousands of dollars worth of property was confiscated. The Civil War was over, and the Union Army was victorious. Harriet and Nelson and the rest of black America were free people when President Abraham Lincoln signed the Emancipation Proclamation (1863) into law. It was a very good year. Nelson well remembered the woman who had captured his heart during wartime.

Harriet remembered that she did anything she could to assist blacks moving into the Auburn-Fleming area by offering shelter until they could find work and a permanent home in either Cayuga County or Canada. She remembered hearing a light but persistent rapping. Harriet strode to the front door. There stood a tall young man; hat in hand and a nearly finished cigar parched his lips. Like so many blacks that were new to the area, he explained that he needed a place to stay and heard that she might possibly assist him. He told her that he was a Civil War veteran and talked a little bit about his service, but he did not immediately tell her that he knew of her from the war. Harriet showed no signs of recognizing the solider, and offered to give him shelter until he found work to provide for himself. A grateful Nelson was shown to a cot in a room on the second level. He was mighty glad to be accepted as a boarder in the house of the woman whom he truly admired. Although he was grateful for her help, love pulled at his heartstrings. Not wanting to further impose on Harriet, Nelson immediately set out to find work.

Harriet recalled that she slowly developed a fondness for

the young man. My goodness, he had to be at least twenty years her junior. She recalled the day, shortly after he moved in, when he stood in the kitchen telling her that he found work as a brick maker at the Pierce brick yard. He was a hard worker and Harriet wasn't eager to let go of a man who contributed so reliably to the household, and Nelson made no real efforts to move on either. They both felt satisfied with each other and developed a strong bond. It was no surprise to those that knew them that they announced that they would be wed. Reverend Henry Fowler married them. It was a small ceremony in the basement of the Central Presbyterian Church in Auburn, several years after the war. Harriet remembered Nelson as a good man and a provider. He was her better half for nearly twenty years.

Nelson was her source of strength when the white frame structure she had always known as home, nearly burned to the ground. The fire began where the stovepipe emerged through the roof. The orange embers gradually ignited into a raging fire. Most of the home was damaged. Nelson knew how much the house meant to Harriet. Not only was it home, but it was a symbol of freedom and a safe haven for family and friends, too. With the assistance of brick makers and bricklayers, Nelson rebuilt the house. The new brick house on the Auburn-Fleming line stood majestically amidst the fruit trees and gardens. A few short years later, Harriet's hard-working husband died from tuberculosis. Harriet buried her husband at Fort Hill Cemetery. Shortly after his death, Harriet filed with the State of New York, County of Cayuga, for her husband's Civil War pension. She eventually received her husband's pension, but never received one for her service in the Civil War.

Harriet continued to swing in her porch swing. The afternoon breeze brushed her brow and drawn cheeks. She rubbed her rough hands around the ends of the wooden arms on the swing and remembered the first love of her life, John Tubman. So much time had passed. Her young love for him seemed like it was a lifetime ago, and it was, but it felt like it was yesterday. John was a free Negro man. When they married in Dorchester County, Maryland, they had no idea that Harriet's mistress intended to sell her into slavery further south. Slavery was slavery wherever it was institutionalized, but slaves were terrified by the horror stories they heard about slaves that were sold. Harriet had no intention of being sold to another plantation. This was her chance to escape. She remembered the fierce need to leave as soon as she could. She and John had been married for five years. They had no children, but John was patient and believed that children would come. She did, too. They were committed to each other, or so she thought.

One of the masters that her father, Ben, worked for named John Trevillion Stewart had forewarned him that Eliza Brodess was in the process of selling off slaves, including Harriet and her brothers, Benjamin and Robert. Eliza needed an infusion of cash to settle debts and maintain her lavish lifestyle in the wake of her husband's death. She would not allow for herself or their nine children to suffer economically one bit.

Harriet confided in her husband that word had traveled that she was to be sold. Before his death, Edward Brodess thought nothing of selling her sisters to some distant plantation. Linah left two children behind and Sophe left one. Harriet was certain that Edward's widow would have no problem, since Harriet had not given birth to any children.

Harriet begged John to escape with her. Harriet's anxiety and tears would not sway him. His mind was made up. There was no way that he was going to jeopardize his free status and be taken down by patrollers and dogs and possibly get killed in the process. The answer was absolutely not. He would not endanger himself for the sake of a` pipedream. He would not divulge her plans to escape, but he had no interest in escaping with her. Even now, so many years later, Harriet felt the pangs of rejection swell within her breast. Fresh tears stung her eyes and rolled down her face. She quickly wiped them away, having learned a long time ago that even the strongest love cannot make a person do something he does not want to do. Harriet felt somewhat naive that she would give it a second try. After her escape, she returned to Dorchester County to convince John of the benefits of a free life in Philadelphia. Her heart was again broken when she discovered that John had taken a new wife, Caroline. The jealousy she felt when she first saw Caroline had long since diminished. Harriet learned several years later that John Tubman had died. In fact, a white neighbor named Robert Vincent murdered him.

That day Robert Vincent and John Tubman had a terrible row over a sack of ashes. There was no way that either one would allow the other to have it. Ashes were a prized commodity in those days. Each man had promised himself that the other would only take possession of the sack over the other's dead body. John's dead body was the price paid for the grey-black soot that was stuffed into the bulging burlap bag.

Within seconds, anger turned into rage and the deadly deed was done. John's son witnessed the tumultuous scene. The young boy belted out a deafening cry and dropped to his knees next to his father's bloody, lifeless body. No amount of sobbing or praying would bring his father back to life. The free black man laid still, as if asleep, never again to recount the story of his family's gift of freedom from their master. The boy was stunned and grief stricken. He ran as fast as his legs could carry him down the dirt road to find comfort in his mother's arms. Caroline's screams could be heard by every neighbor within earshot. The cry was unmistakable. Tragedy had struck the Tubman home.

The courthouse was filled to the rafters. Blacks and whites from each corner of the county settled in to witness the trial of Robert Vincent. An all white jury was impaneled. The blacks hoped against hope that justice would be served, but few trusted that it ever would. As the criminal proceedings began, a hush permeated the stifling courtroom. Beads of sweat drenched the faces and necks of those in attendance. Kerchiefs and paper fans did little to abate the heat and humidity.

The judge, prosecutor, jury, and the defense attorney instinctively knew that the trial would not last long. They had never known of—and nor would it have been tolerated—that a white man would be convicted of murdering a black man. Robert and his trusted attorney were confident that Robert would not spend one minute in confinement for this heinous act. After the character witnesses had been cross-examined and the evidence presented, the direction in which the trial was headed was clear. The defense claimed that Vincent's life was threatened and that the murder of John Tubman was a result of self-defense. An enraged black man threatened to kill his client over a sack of ashes and Vincent was left with no choice other than to club the avenger to death. The bloody club that rendered another otherwise healthy man lifeless was never to be found. The son saw the club next to his dead father. Others who happened upon the scene saw it, too. As chance would have it, the evidence had been mysteriously removed. Even with the evidence of the bloody club, the declaration of a white man claiming to protect his life from the threat of violence from a black man would be easily upheld. In the absence of this evidence, it was a certain acquittal. The whites receded from the courtroom confident that justice had prevailed. The blacks knew that, once again, the life of a black man was not valued. The loss of husband and father was not thoroughly prosecuted and avenged, and there was little hope that it ever would be. John was buried with his dreams, successes, and failures, like any man. The only difference was that his life had ended prematurely at the hands of a white man who would not pay the price for killing a black man over a sack of ashes. Harriet grew solemn. She long ago became friends with the fact that John's feelings for her had changed the night she escaped. Her heart swelled with sympathy for Caroline and the children. Harriet prayed that they had learned to accept his death and life without him as she was forced to do. Poor, poor John. The words escaped as a murmur through Harriet's dried lips.

Harriet's heartbeat quickened as her mind was flooded with memories of Bucktown, her birthplace on the Eastern Shore of Maryland. No different from the rest of the slaves, she was treated hard. Hard work. Hard times. Separation of family. Death and illness. It was the strength of her parents and siblings that made her life worth living. To see their faces, to hear their voices, and to cherish their embraces warmed her spirit and let her know that there was more to life than slavery. In a fleeting moment, the values of her parents washed over her. Above all, give praise and glory to God, take care of one another, and help others who are in need. Harriet felt good that she could honestly say that she did all of these things. She had committed her life to her God, her family, and her people. If the good Lord were to take her now, she believed with all of her heart and soul that she had fulfilled the family legacy. In her mind's eye, she envisioned that she would see the face of Jesus on her last day. Her body shuttered in anticipation of experiencing that ecstasy.

Harriet was quickly reminded that she did have personal failings and foibles. While she knew that God's divine plan had its orderly outworking in her life, she often felt that she should have done more to find her siblings Linah, Sophe, Harry, and Moses. Linah and Sophe had been sold, which forced them to leave their children behind without the tenderness of a mother's love and guidance. Harry and Moses had escaped from the Brodess plantation as soon as they were able. Through the grapevine, the family heard that the both of them were safe. Harry was a mariner working for Levin Stewart in his shipbuilding business, and Moses was a laborer and farmer. Moses returned to Dorchester County after the Civil War with his wife, Julia, and their children, Harriet and Benjamin. Both of the children were named after his mother and father. Harriet's greatest wish was that she would have rescued them and that they too could have found the taste of freedom in the North. Harriet resigned herself to the fact that the greatest blessing was that her brothers were safe. The family took comfort in the hope that God's plan included that Linah and Sophe's lives had been spared and that they were alive and well. Harriet was humbled knowing that she had heeded God's instruction to rescue her aging parents, three brothers—Robert, Benjamin, and Henry—two nieces, Anne Marie and

Margaret, and scores of others from the jaws of slavery. Harriet also regretted that her sister Mary Ann had died before she was able to reach her.

Harriet played the scenes from her life over and over again in her mind. She concluded that her life experiences were fraught with challenges, successes, worries, joyful moments, danger, security, deaths, and births. Throughout it all, trust and honesty were so very important. She believed that she was a trustworthy person. Some might have claimed that she was dishonest, because her life's work involved illegal activity. It was illegal to steal away the human property of plantation owners, but Harriet knew she had a higher calling. She knew from the depths of her soul that she had been called to do God's work. She knew that her calling was a moral one that superseded the greed and selfishness of plantation owners and a slave economy run amok. Harriet knew the trust of her family and friends, neighbors, agents of the road, members of the Vigilance Committee, and undoubtedly, the people that she rescued. She often boasted that she had never lost a passenger on the Underground Railroad.

Trust was incredibly important. Harriet knew that her passengers, or her brood, as she referred to them, put their lives in her hand. They trusted her on faith and her track record. Few of them knew her personally, but they were willing to have Moses transport them from a life of slavery to one of freedom. The abolitionists of that era often commented on the true grit of the freedom seekers. There was no question in anyone's mind that they had arrived at one of the most risky decisions that enslaved Negroes could make. They would risk life and limb to escape to free land in Canada. Men and women, with their children, sought to leave bondage behind;

they desired a new life—a new life that would present new opportunities for them and for their children. Harriet Tubman made this dream come true for tens of slaves.

Now, Harriet's attention was focused on the many slaves that she had rescued. Her mind lingered on each brood. For a moment, there was a collage of faces. Young, old, dark, fair, suckling babes, and wide-eyed children were not certain of what lay ahead of them, but all were willing to risk the journey. Most of Harriet's rescues took place while she lived in St. Catharines, Canada. An escaped slave herself, she knew what her passengers were thinking and feeling. She knew that beneath their desire for freedom lurked feelings of fear and uncertainty. She did her best to belay their fears by making it clear that she was in charge. There would be no second-guessing her instructions or her directions. Once they were on the road, there would be no turning back. She would not allow any of them to put the rest of them at risk of being captured or killed. At the outset of each journey, she brandished her rifle to demonstrate that if she had to she would use it to keep them safe. Harriet knew there would be tense moments for fear of going further. It happened on nearly every rescue. She also knew that the light of freedom would greet them at the end of the journey. Praying together, singing hymns, and story-telling helped to keep them focused on the mission.

One rescue came immediately to mind. It was Harriet's last rescue. She made her way from her home in Fleming, New York, to Maryland. About four months before the start of the Civil War, Harriet left the brisk and chilly weather of Upstate New York for the less frosty region of her home state. She knew from agents on the road that the Ennets family was ready to be rescued. She had made this trip so many times before that there were no surprises. She began each roundtrip journey armed with the faith that she was doing God's work. She also had the support of sympathizers and supporters of the Underground Railroad. With this rescue and so many others, her good friend Thomas Garrett of Wilmington, Delaware, provided food, clothing, and financial assistance to secure a successful rescue.

Stephen Ennets and his wife, Maria, were no longer willing to accept being forced to live apart from each other. Theirs was a condition that was very common in slavery. Stephen, a slave owned by John Kaiger, was not allowed to live with his wife. Maria lived eight miles away on the Algier Pearcy Plantation. Maria worked for him for ten dollars a year. The Ennets had three children who lived with their mother and would certainly be hired out by Pearcy when they were of an age to do so. To the parents, this was unthinkable. Both were very astute. Stephen and Maria wanted to liberate their children from this fate. The older of the children were Harriet, who was six-years-old, and Amanda, who was four-years-old. The youngest was an infant of three-months-old. Knowing their neighborhood well, Harriet went into the bowels of slavery for the last time to free the Ennets. Joining them was a young man named John. Harriet was confident that if she could get them as far as Wilmington, Delaware, Thomas Garrett would make arrangements to get them to free territory in Chester, Pennsylvania.

It was not an easy rescue. The family wanted to come through at a time when the established road was under the vigilance of slave catchers more than ever before. The threat of capture was palpable. Harriet remembered how grateful she was that after a perilous voyage she was, once again, able to deliver this young family and John to Wilmington. Another woman arriving from Baltimore joined the Ennets and John. It was not unusual for freedom seekers coming from more than one area to meet in Delaware, and continue the journey to Canada together. Harriet thought of all of them now. It had been at least fifty years since that rescue. She had spent ten years of her life liberating freedom seekers. She had never lost one of them. She wondered what had become of the Ennets, John, the woman from Baltimore, and all of the other newly freed slaves. Did they find what they were looking for? Was the taste of freedom as sweet as they had imagined? Would they conclude, as she had, that even with its trial and tribulations, freedom was their God-given right and worthy of winning? Her greatest hope was that they had fully experienced the good fight and victory over the evil system of slavery. She was comforted by the thought of knowing that they would live a good and productive life if they held onto their faith, worked hard, and never turned a blind eye to helping others. Harriet was certain that one-by-one, family-by-family, community-by-community, blacks could live free and prosper. Trusting God, each other, and human-rights sympathizers was as necessary in a free life as was bread and water.

Harriet chuckled to herself. She stopped herself from breaking into a downright raucous guffaw. She was known for her hearty laugh. Harriet thought that she could size up a dishonest person in no time. A word or gesture would reveal dishonesty lurking behind steely eyes or a sheepish smile. Yet this time, she missed it altogether. Two men (one was dark and one was yellow) gained her confidence, stole a great deal of money from her, and left her half dead in an alleyway. It was one of the most painful and embarrassing times in her life. She could still feel the deep regret she had for using her trustworthiness to involve her brother John Stewart and the good men of Auburn in such a shameless situation. Now, she could laugh about it. It was simply a silly, silly mistake.

As memory recalled the incident, two men had recently arrived in Auburn from South Carolina, or so they claimed. It was not often, even in the North, that you would find two colored men traveling together with a common purpose. The dark one was Harris, alias John Thomas. The yellow one was Stephenson, alias Johnson. They told folks that they were determined to find work in the North and settle there. This caused no real suspicion, since many people passed through small towns in search for greater opportunities. In time, the two made the acquaintance of Harriet Tubman Davis and her brother John. The traveling duo seemed friendly enough and engaged them more and more. The two even mentioned knowing her grandnephew Alfred Bowley who lived in South Carolina. Harriet decided that before they left town she would offer them a simple meal. So, she invited them to the homestead. Without hesitation, the men accepted her gracious invitation.

The fare consisted of stewed chicken, carrots and potatoes with biscuits and fried apples. An occasional flea had to be swatted away, but that did nothing to take away from the fact that the meal was thoroughly satisfying to the palate. The chicken bones were sucked clean and the last drop of stew in their bowls was sopped up with the remaining biscuits. There was more than enough left for Nelson, who would be returning soon from the brickyard. The men thanked Harriet for the delicious meal. Harriet accepted the compliment, feeling good that she had provided the men with a decent meal, since she understood that they would be leaving the area in the next couple of days. Not knowing whether she would ever see them again, Harriet wished them Godspeed and success in their travels. John, who didn't say much throughout the meal, nodded in agreement with his sister's well wishes.

The natural light streaming through the back door to the kitchen had begun to dim. Dusk would soon descend. The men gave each other a knowing glance that said, "These two will do just fine." Before rising from the roughhewn table, the men told Harriet and John that they wanted to share a money-making opportunity with them. They told them they would only share this chance-of-a-lifetime with folks that they trusted. Even though they only knew Harriet and John for a short while, as far as they were concerned they were good people, and there were no two other folks in the area that they trusted more. The more the men talked the more interested the brother and sister became. Both Harriet and John knew that a little extra money would sure make things a lot easier. John and his wife, Minnie, could use it for the supplies he needed on his property, which was located near the South Street tollgate. Harriet knew that the wad of dollars she kept hidden in the hem of her shirt was dwindling. It would not hurt would it to have some extra money set aside to care for those around her? She had always trusted that God would provide. The men promised her $240 as the negotiator and an additional award for delivering a customer. Harriet was confident that this was all part of God's plan.

In an excited but hushed manner, the yellow man continued with the story. He spoke with great bravado, but his lips tried to hide several broken teeth. He went on to describe how the traveling duo had acquired quite a bit of gold. They confessed that the gold belonged to the government and was obtained after the war. There was enough gold to fill a strong box about three-feet long and twenty-inches high. Harriet and John could not believe it. They had heard about gold, but they had never seen any. The dark man went on to say that there had to be at least 2,000 dollars-worth of gold in the box. The yellow man confided that what they feared most was that the gold would be stolen if they continued to travel with it. They needed to cash it in. Government agents were probably already on their tails. The men had decided that they needed to sell the gold before they left town. With confidence in their new-found friends, the men begged Harriet and John to think of anyone that might help them accomplish this. Harriet was momentarily stunned, and John simply had no idea. Neither one had any connection or accounts with the banks. The men pushed them further to think of anyone, white or black, that might buy the gold.

Harriet thought long and hard. She had become quite well known in Auburn, because of her work on the Underground Railroad. Over the years, she had the distinct pleasure of meeting and becoming very friendly with many of the prominent families in Auburn. Most of the men were business owners, attorneys, big farmers, or real estate owners. Long before she took residence in Auburn, they were sympathizers with her work as a freedom fighter. They supported the Underground Railroad and helped finance the movement of freedom seekers from the South to Auburn to Canada prior to the end of the Civil War. She had friends who supported the cause, including the Bradfords, Osbornes, Sewards, Pomeroys, and Telfords. Many of them used their financial resources and their homes as safe havens to usher black folks to freedom.

With this particular situation, Harriet decided to contact several bankers, capitalists, and a colored pastor to get their interest in the gold deal. She called upon the former sheriff, James Mead, who discouraged her from having any further dealing with the men. He suspected that they were robbers, and Harriet was likely putting her life at risk. He wanted nothing to do with it. She then called on Dr. E.P.K. Smith and C.A. Myers both of whom were somewhat interested. They were willing to offer $500 and give the balance once they could determine that the gold was genuine. They went out to Harriet's place to meet the men. They were not convinced.

There was also Mr. Bell who was suspicious, but he wanted to hear more. Bell had heard of a Frank Madden from St. Catharines, Canada, who was robbed of $500. In that affair, the gold man told Madden that he had a box of gold hidden at the Suspension Bridge, but he could not get it over to the Canadian side. The gold man was adamant that he had to exchange the gold for currency as soon as possible. The colored man did feel that he could not personally use the yellow metal without causing suspicion. Madden met with the man in the room where the gold was supposed to be. The box was there. He handed over $500. Conveniently, the colored man said that he had forgotten the key and would go get it immediately. The gold man left in a rush, and was never to be seen again. Madden and other Canadian purchasers broke open the box. The opened box revealed the so-called gold. They had just purchased a box filled with layers of stone wrapped neatly with cotton.

Bell listened while the colored men told their story. It was an interesting encounter. The yellow man described in detail how they met in South Carolina. They came north by way of

Charleston to Newbern and Norfolk. They were transported then to New York City. There, they met up with a colored man by the name of Bowers. He successfully gained the interest of a bank cashier, but the white man wanted to see the gold before he handed over the money. The gold men became suspicious of the cashier, and Stephenson put the former slave and the box into a trunk and brought them as baggage to Rome, New York. From there, they settled in Seneca Falls. Bell wanted to see the gold, too. He would not give over any greenbacks unless he saw the gold first. Again, the colored men became suspicious. The potential deal failed.

John Stewart finally decided to speak with Mr. Anthony Shimer. He had known Shimer for many years and trusted him implicitly. He was an easy man to know and one who seemed to welcome new and different things. He was particularly interested in a safe speculation. He was finally convinced to purchase the gold by Harriet herself. She was confident that the colored men could be held to their word. Because of his trust in Harriet's reputation for honesty, he decided to invest in what he believed to be a deal, which promised prolific gain. Although other businessmen tried their best to dissuade him from getting involved, Anthony Shimer withdrew $2,000 from the City Bank to seal the deal.

In October, on that fateful Wednesday afternoon, a procession of horse-drawn carriages pulled up to the tavern past Fleming Hill at Smith's Corner. Shimer and a few other businessmen descended upon the meeting place to witness the success of the transaction. They waited until Harriet and her brother John arrived. John took on added expense to hire a horse and carriage for the two of them. The cost was justified because he believed that he would be reimbursed with a sum of currency that would more than compensate him. When Harriet arrived, she met briefly with Shimer. He counted out the $2,000 and handed it to the famed Conductor of the Underground Railroad. She placed the greenbacks in her apron. Stephenson—of the gold deal duo—met her there.

Harriet and Stephenson left the tavern and walked about a quarter of a mile away toward the lake. Along the way, they passed a house where colored folks lived. Stephenson went in to get Thomas. The two joined Harriet and they made their way across plowed fields and over two fences. Harriet asked where the gold was and the two men pointed to an area not far off. They trudged through the woods, and finally came upon the spot where the trunk was buried. The site was covered with rails. Harriet and the men stooped down to remove the rails. The trunk was buried in the ground well enough to hide its top. The top was covered with leaves. The men commenced to dislodge the canvas-covered box. They lifted the box and placed it next to the opening. The three of them stood over the area, and the dark man became excitable. He demanded to have the greenbacks. Harriet resisted. She would not give them up until she saw the gold. She held on tightly to the wad of currency that was tied securely inside of her apron.

The men stepped away a short distance from the box. Harriet bent down and tried to lift the box. She found it difficult to move. She felt assured that the box contained the gold. The men returned saying that they had forgotten the key. The dark man had also decided that he could not conduct business with her; he would have to speak to the man who put up the money. While explaining why he had come to that decision, Harriet remembered that he passed his hands over her face and chest, instantly she fell to her knees clinging to the small trunk. He had applied a sufficient dose of chloroform.

Harriet awoke groggy. She strained to remember what had happened. All she knew was that the opened trunk (which was full of stones) was there, but the greenbacks were missing. Something terrible had happened. The men were nowhere in sight. She found herself gagged and bound. She knew she had to get back to the tavern. She had been gone much too long. She was able to free her hands that were bound with her shawl and pull the rumbled kerchief out of her mouth. Harriet rolled and crawled over the fields, and then made her way over the fences by placing her chin on the top rail and tumbling over them. She finally arrived alongside of the tavern in a painful heap.

Shimer and a few others were nervous by now and realized that Harriet should have returned. They sauntered outside to get some air. While trying to settle their nervousness, they heard animal-like sounds piercing the nighttime air. They approached the area from where the sounds came. In the darkness, they found a body crawling along the ground.

Upon closer inspection, Shimer shrieked out, "Harriet is that you?" He was answered with a laborious groan. Shimer and the others were shaken to find that this strong and courageous woman was reduced to a heap of shambled humanness sounding like a hurt animal. They found her almost speechless with the kerchief still securely tied around her head. There was also an abrasion across one side of her face.

Not far from where the greenback fiasco occurred, Harriet's husband took her to Sherwood's Corners where she stayed at the home of her longtime friend Slocum Howland to recover from her injuries. Slocum was a Quaker, staunch abolitionist, and merchant. The Howlands and many other Quakers in the Poplar Ridge area of Cayuga County were involved in the anti-slavery movement, women's rights, and Indian land rights. Slocum was known to use his home, store, and boating business to usher freedom seekers through Cayuga County to Canada. His grown children, William and Emily, and his granddaughter Isabel were similarly committed to human rights. Having heard of the disastrous affair with the gold man and her painful condition, Slocum offered to house Harriet until she was able to resume her normal habits.

Reflecting on that time, Harriet remembered enduring it as one of embarrassment, and for a long while, she felt like a spectacle. Some in the community may have had sympathy for her, but she knew that she and Anthony Shimer were the laughing stocks of the business community. They had been duped in a major way. There were no two ways about it. Her brother John, who could least afford it, found himself at a loss of work and money for hiring the horse and buggy to travel to Smith's Corner that fateful day. Shimer insisted that Harriet and John had agreed to insure him against any loss of money. The two of them didn't have ten greenbacks in their pockets, let alone $2,000. They were certain that they were headed for ruin. Fearful that he would get nothing, Shimer accepted John's team of horses as payment against his loss.

It was now approaching dusk. Harriet's old bones were becoming a little stiff. She had spent too much time reminiscing. Looking back on the good and the bad, she felt that life was really very good. She also had to admit that it was full of lessons. She had come a long way since her days on the Brodess Plantation in Bucktown, Maryland. The trials and tribulations did not trump her God-inspired life, her loving relationships, her friendships, and her successes. Sighing as she lifted her small frame from the porch swing, Harriet knew tomorrow would come soon enough. Taking her good ole' time to get into the house, she wondered what was left in the pot on the stove.

Harriet Tubman Davis and her husband, Nelson Davis, who was a Civil War veteran. Also pictured is presumably their "adopted" daughter Gertie Davis at the home on South Street Road.

Harriet Ross Tubman Davis pictured about a year before her death. She lived a full and fulfilling life. Harriet Tubman Davis died at ninety-two-years-old.

CHAPTER THIRTY

—

The Harriet Tubman Home

England Norris, the tax assessor for Fleming, New York, purchased the Harriet Tubman home for one dollar. He owned a large tract of land further south on South Street, and he was known to be a shrewd businessman. The solid brick structure with a kitchen and seven rooms no longer belonged to the Tubman heirs.

The Tubman family referred to the brick house on South Street Road as their home. Even during the lean times, there was always something to eat from the pot on the wood-burning stove. Somehow Aunt Harriet showed up with something for the pot. There was always a constant aroma of food lingering in the air of the first-floor rooms that reminded one of down-home cooking. As with any household, laughter, sadness, hard work, marriages, births, and deaths had crossed its threshold. Every friend and family member who had the opportunity to live there, even if for a short while, grew to love the house, the grounds, and the freedom that went along with it. From swimming in the pond to harvesting vegetables from the garden to chopping wood for the stove, fond memories abounded. These memories were especially bittersweet for Harriet's grandniece Mary Gaskin. Having just laid her Aunt

Harriet to rest, she searched her mind for as many sweet memories as she could find. For every sweet one she found, a bitter one crept in behind it. Now in her mid-forties, she realized that it was all a part of life. You had to be grateful for the good times, and learn from the bad times. She came to know that both kinds of experiences reinforced the values that she had learned from her family. The most important of which were to be faithful to the Creator, take care of one another, help others whenever possible, and never shy away from hard work.

The death of Harriet Tubman, although expected because of her advancing age and ill health, stunned the communities of Fleming and Auburn. They would miss her walking north on South Street Road toward the center of town. That familiar profile of a small dark woman dressed in dark clothing with an old dark hat covering her white crinkly hair would no longer be seen against the rural backdrop on the outskirts of Auburn. The kitchen help of the wealthy white families would no longer see her perched on the back porch steps, waiting for the audience of the mistress of the house. There was one young Irish immigrant maid at the Pomeroy household that Harriet especially liked. Both found a way to communicate with each other. At the end of their visit, the young one and the old one knew that they had developed a real friendship. Harriet's raucous laughter and lively hand gestures elicited happy responses from children and adults alike. Harriet was a character in her own right. There was no one quite like her. She was Aunt Harriet to all and she would be sorely missed.

No one felt her absence more than Mary. Pangs of sadness pummeled beneath her breast. She understood how simply her aunt lived, but she also knew how complicated that life was.

Her aunt worked until her aging body just could not go on any further. Yet, up to that point, she found a way to provide freedom, food, clothing, shelter, and healthcare to any black person in need. Her aunt Harriet was always shown a blessing from God through the good deeds of others. Almost every need was provided for, not for herself, but for those in her charge. She did not, at times, have enough money to cover her expenses. In faith, she knew that God would provide. Without fail, money would come to her, mostly through the generosity of Christians and Quakers in the area. Although her aunt's greatest asset was the family homestead, Harriet Tubman died penniless with a number of debts to creditors, including family, and to the tax authorities.

At the ripe old age of seventy-five, Harriet purchased an additional twenty-five acres of land adjoining her seven acres of land. The newly purchased property belonged to John Farmer prior to his death. She had great hopes for the property. The majority of the land was located in Auburn, and a smaller portion was located in Fleming. She was fortunate to have become the owner of several buildings on that property. The one of greatest interest to her was the large brick building in the back on the Fleming side of her newly acquired land. Years prior there was a functional brickyard "way up in the back" of the property. The large brick building was used as a dormitory to house the brickmakers domiciled there. Harriet's vision was to utilize the vacant building to house aging and infirmed Negroes, providing them with a roof over their heads and a staff to attend to their healthcare needs. She named the building after her good friend, humanitarian, and abolitionist, John Brown. Harriet depended, as usual, on the generosity of her benefactors to keep the doors open. Even in her twilight years, she was determined to care for her people in whatever way she could. She recognized a growing need for the frail and elderly, and she wanted them, mostly former slaves, to transition to the other side with dignity and respect.

It was a very ambitious endeavor. Harriet realized, after a time, that even with the financial support she received from many people of goodwill and the pension money she received from her husband's Civil War service, she was not able to effectively sustain and maintain the John Brown Home for the Aged and Indigent Colored People. Several years before her death, she deeded the twenty-five acres and the nursing home to the A.M.E Zion Church to own and operate in accordance to her mission of providing for the needy. Under the direction of the board of managers, the facility was renamed the Harriet Tubman Home for the Aged. The church continued its service to the aged and infirmed for years. The first nursing home for Negroes was beset with many challenges to keep the doors open, and the A.M.E. Church eventually closed the facility. The building was eventually taken by fire.

Although the Harriet Tubman Home for the Aged no longer exists, the A.M.E Zion Church still owns the property on which it stood. The Church and the Harriet Tubman Foundation manage the grounds and the remaining structures on the property. The white house with the veranda (near the road) on the Auburn side of South Street has been named the Harriet Tubman Home. It functions as a museum and houses family artifacts and photographs for the viewing public, but it is not the original site of the John Brown Home for the Aged or the Harriet Tubman Home for the Aged or Harriet Tubman's residence. Community lore has it that Negroes who needed a temporary home lived in the white house on South

Street Road. Harriet Tubman lived in the brick house just to the south on the other side of the Auburn-Fleming tollgate. The tollgate no longer exists. In years gone by, it appeared to separate one side of the thirty-two acres from the other. Currently, the structure designated as the Harriet Tubman Home is available to the public for programs following the Annual Harriet Tubman Gravesite Pilgrimage, Home for the Aged Tours, family reunions, and other community events.

My grandmother Mary Elliott Gaskin worked as a matron, laundress, and cook at the John Brown Home for the Aged. She worked side-by-side with her aunt, the nurses, and attendants to care for the less fortunate. The residents, or inmates as they were also called, were well cared for. Now, in the wake of the death of one of the greatest heroines and abolitionists in American history, Mary was named as one of heirs to the Tubman home and seven acres of land on the Auburn-Fleming line. Two other heirs, Katie Stewart and Frances Smith, were also named. Katie Stewart, another grandniece, was the daughter of Harriet's nephew John Issac Stewart. John was the son of her brother William Henry Stewart. Frances Smith was a good friend and the wife of Harriet's confidante and minister Reverend Charles A.U. Smith. For more than fifty years, Harriet's pride and joy was her homestead and land. She left her greatest asset to the three women who were closest to her.

After being "brung up" on a Southern plantation and having the good fortune to be free and own property, Harriet knew that she was blessed. From living in a one-room shanty to a seven-room house, one could say it was surreal. Her seven acres symbolized hearth, home, and freedom. It was a constant reminder of her life achievements. From her vegetable gardens to her apple and peach trees to her chickens and to the geese, raccoons, and woodchucks that inhabited the grounds, who could have asked for more? She was forever grateful and indebted to her Lord and Master, and William H. Seward for the place she called home. Harriet always held a special place in her heart for William and his wife, Frances. The two represented what was so good about Christians and Quakers who abhorred the institution of slavery. Land and home ownership was a dream come true for former slaves, including Harriet Tubman. The Sewards made it happen.

Harriet Tubman had no children of her own. In addition to the three women who were closest to her, there were a number of grandnieces and grandnephews that were related by blood through her brothers and sisters. Harriet Tubman's executor, Louis K.R. Laird, filed the appropriate legal notices. Each relative was notified of the death and the last will and testament regarding her property. There was no contest. Family members Clarence and Alida Stewart were identified as creditors in the administrative papers filed with the will. The documents indicated that they would be reimbursed a little more than $500 for monies spent on Harriet's medical care.

Harriet Tubman Davis died on March 10, 1913. She took her last breath in Fleming, New York, at the John Brown Home for the Aged, after a long bout with chronic bronchitis and senility. On that last day, she saw the face of Jesus, as did the indigent who were left in her charge, as well as her brother William Henry Stewart who died several months before. Harriet and her younger brother, William Henry, were buried next to each other in Fort Hill Cemetery. The grand dame of Auburn was laid to rest on March 13, 1913.

CHAPTER THIRTY-ONE

—

The Norris House

England Norris knew a good deal when he saw it. An immigrant from England, Norris had become a very successful businessman in Fleming. He also held the position of tax assessor for the town of Fleming. He owned thirty acres of his own land and had just acquired seven more just north of his property. Norris and Harriet Tubman's attorney, Louis K.R. Laird, filed the paperwork and initiated the legal process. Norris was positioned to buy the home of Harriet Tubman at South Street Road.

The proceedings were rather cut-and-dried. A critical transaction at that time was to ensure that the legal heirs quitclaim the property. It was a very sad day when Mary Gaskin, Katy Stewart, and Frances Smith reluctantly quitclaimed their legal rights to the property of the deceased heroine. Each one did this with a heavy heart, because so many of their personal memories were tied to the land and the brick house out there on South Street Road. It very quickly became most evident that the women did not have enough money to settle the debts and back taxes held against the estate. The A.M.E. Church also was not in a financial position to purchase the property. They had their hands full with maintaining the twenty-five acres and the John Brown Home for the Aged on the adjoining property. Rumor had it that the heirs did not want the church to have the property. Truth be told, the heirs had no control over the sale of the Tubman land. After he paid all of the outstanding debts against the property, England Norris bought the Harriet Tubman Home for one dollar.

England Norris had his eye on the property for quite some time. He was well aware of Harriet's advancing age and illness. He had designs on the land. England's son, Frank, was newly married. He wanted Frank and his bride, Edith, to live on the newly acquired property. England relished the idea of having his family living close by to him and his wife, Ellen. Once Norris acquired the property, he deeded it over to his son. That was the beginning of more than seventy years of the Norris family inhabiting the house that was once known as Aunt Harriet's place.

Shortly after the newlyweds moved in, England Norris held an estate sale to sell Harriet Tubman's possessions. On that spring day in 1916, all of Aunt Harriet's goods that were in saleable condition were a cherry bedroom suite with spring and mattress, a cherry bed stand, porch swing, hammock, reading lamp, parlor lamp, gas oven, lawn mower, wire and windows for a chicken coop, a brick cottage, and fruit jars. One could only imagine how often the fruit jars had been filled with applesauce and peach marmalade by the hands of the great Conductor of the Underground Railroad.

Frank and Edith raised six children in the two-story brick house that stood on the Auburn-Fleming line. Seward, Hazel, Dorothy, Harry, Donald, and Ruth did not want for much growing up in rural Cayuga County. The children took full advantage of the seasons, from playing in the meadow to picking apples to ice-skating on the frozen pond. The girls helped their mother tend to the flower gardens that she loved so much. The boys especially enjoyed helping their father trap muskrats and raccoons. Life was good on South Street Road. On any day, the children could visit their grandparents who lived on the same side of the street down the road apiece. It had all worked out just the way that England had engineered it.

As Frank's children grew older and finished school, each one left the nest one by one. Donald and Harry enlisted in the armed services during World War II. The sisters all found husbands and chose professions similar to those of the other young adults of their age. After the war, Donald and Harry returned to Fleming to work in their father's successful trucking business. They delivered everything from dry goods to furniture to their commercial and residential customers.

When Harry Norris returned from the war, he married his sweetheart, Alice Cost. Alice was born in Syracuse and was brought to Auburn by her father after her mother's sudden death during the 1918 pneumonia epidemic. Alice attended schools in Auburn where she met her husband-to-be, and she became very close friends with his sister Ruth. Once Harry and Alice married, they moved into the family homestead for a few years. Frank and Harry decided that business was going so well that Harry should remain nearby. To keep his son and his son's wife near to home and business, Frank deeded one acre of the seven-acre property to Harry and Alice. The arrangement was perfect. Harry was eligible for a veteran's program that secured homebuilding materials for returning veterans at no cost. It took several years, but Harry built a smaller brick house for his bride next door to his parents. They raised their son Edward in the home.

The delivery business continued to grow and the Norrises diversified and opened the Norris Delivery Co. With a standing contract with the Auburn School District, they transported students to school, including those who were wheelchair bound. The school bus operation, like the trucking business, was housed in the barn behind the house.

The years seemed to fly by. England and Ellen were elderly and needed more day-to-day assistance. Ellen was eventually put into a nursing home where she died. Shortly afterward, old man Norris sold his property, business, and real estate holdings and moved into the home of his son, Frank. The once vibrant and shrewd businessman, who had accomplished most of what he wanted to in life, was now frail and white haired. Frank, Edith, Harry, and Alice did everything they could to make him comfortable. Their father and grandfather enjoyed spending time on the side porch, which by that time had been enclosed. He liked everything in its place and tidy. Alice took it as a great compliment, when he repeatedly told her that she was a good cleaner. Not long after he came to live on South Street Road, England required around-the-clock nursing care, and he, too, was taken to the nursing home where he died.

Life went on as it always does. Frank and Edith's adult children were now married and raising children of their own. Alice and Harry had one son, Edward, who grew up learning about the family business and attending Auburn schools. He enjoyed the added advantage of growing up next door to his grandparents. School, playtime, and chores consumed most of his time.

His grandparent's home had not been the residence of the Moses of her People for more than fifty years, but the community's memory was slow to fade. Edward often heard stories about the famous freedom fighter. As a young lad, he occasionally asked his father, Harry, about the renowned Conductor of the Underground Railroad, but found that probing questions were not encouraged. In fact, it was taboo for anyone in the family to even mention the name Harriet Tubman and the fact that she previously owned the property. Mother Edith was adamant about it.

On occasion, even Mother Edith failed to abide by her own rules. It was infrequent, but she shared some information about Harriet Tubman with her family. The little that she knew of the abolitionist was that she loved sitting on the side porch, which adjoined her property to the north. It was the same side porch that the patriarch England Norris enjoyed so much. The view from that side of the house was spectacular and allowed one a great view of the neighboring twenty-five acres of land. The porch was one of Harriet Tubman's favorite places. She would observe the white house she owned on that side of the property. She would sit for hours watching the activities of the Negro boarders that she allowed to live there. The white house and several other structures, including the John Brown Home for the Aged, could be seen in the distance. Mother Edith also mentioned that Harriet was known to have a large vegetable garden. She would walk miles on a daily basis as far south as Scipio selling her produce. After her death, Negroes from the white house were known to cross over the open field to the then Norris property and steal eggs during the night.

Over the years, the family grew to understand why Mother Edith seemingly had such disdain for anyone talking about Harriet Tubman. What at first blush might have been interpreted as disdain was later recognized as a protectionist measure she took on behalf of her family and home. She firmly believed that Harriet Tubman's notoriety grew so rapidly after her death that she was afraid their home would become a spectacle. In her mind's eye, she could envision throngs of people standing outside, day in and day out, gawking and taking pictures. She was fearful that inquiring reporters and researchers would badger her and her husband. She was afraid that people would take anything from the property that was not nailed down and thought to be of historical value. She even went so far as to not allow the children to go into the attic. The attic remained closed throughout their childhood. Some might say that her obstinacy bordered on paranoia. All Edith wanted was a simple family life in the house that was once Harriet's. By hook or by crook, that was the way it was going to be. There would be no markers or historical placards posted on her property to identify it as the original home of Harriet Tubman. Edith's wishes were abided by.

After Harriet's death, Edith and Frank saw so many changes to the land next door, which had been deeded by Harriet to the A.M.E. Church. The white house set back from the road became the parsonage of the presiding pastors. Each pastor was the caretaker of the house and the property. It was a small-frame house originally, but it was refurbished after a major fire. The structure was made larger and a front veranda was added. The local congregation, to which Harriet Tubman and many relatives belonged, found it difficult to pay for repairs and the upkeep of the property. Over the years, the A.M.E. District Bishops needed the house and the property to generate enough money to partially cover its expenses. It was thought that a revenue stream could be established by opening the grounds to the public. There was no way to predict if or when the original home of Harriet would ever belong to the church given the Norrises' hands-off position. So, it was decided that the first floor of the white house would be renovated and turned into a small museum that would house artifacts, photographs, furniture, and period pieces mostly donated by family members. The white house down South Street Road was designated the Harriet Tubman Home.

Syracuse University invested a considerable amount of faculty and student resources from the anthropology department to conduct anthropological digs to uncover and confirm the historical veracity of the Tubman property and its historical structures. The tourism prospects were not as robust as predicted, but the historical and financial significance of the Auburn and Fleming sides of the property were and are of great interest and investment for the church and the Harriet Tubman Foundation. The then New York Senator Hillary Rodham Clinton and the National Park Service have also shown an interest in securing funding and providing resources for the property.

The aging Edith and Frank Norris and their family decided to sell the original home of Harriet Tubman. There was great interest by the community and the church as to who would acquire the Tubman Home and the original six of seven acres upon which it stood.

It had been more than eighty years since the Church was deeded the greater portion of the Tubman property. In that time, the real estate value of the property had appreciated significantly. The church was intent on becoming the owner. It would not be an easy feat. The down payment and the mortgage would be sizeable. Could the church acquire and maintain the Tubman residence? The church decided that the investment was greater than the threat of losing the property and made a purchase offer. Like any real-estate buyer, the church waited with baited breath until they learned that the Norris family accepted the purchase offer. The church and the Norris family closed on the property. The original Harriet Tubman Home now belonged to the church.

The remaining Norris with historical ties to the property was Alice Norris. Alice was the owner of the last acre of land originally owned by Harriet Tubman. Her husband, Harry, and her son, Edward, predeceased her. Alice was well-known in the Auburn-Fleming communities. She did not hesitate to talk about her marriage into the Norris family, the growth of their businesses, and what it was like to actually live for a few years in the house owned by Harriet Tubman. For years she attended public hearings and events regarding Harriet Tubman and the property that she owned. She also participated in the Annual Harriet Tubman Gravesite Pilgrimage. Alice also conducted her own research and compiled a collection of documents and articles about her family ties to the Conductor of the Underground Railroad.

Alice Cost Norris passed away on October 29, 2010. Her family put the "last acre" up for sale. Although my daughter Michele and her husband were not successful in acquiring the property, it was our distinct pleasure to have known Alice.

Rest in peace, my friend.

— *The End* —

Alice Norris (left) enjoying lunch at Kosta's in Auburn, New York, with Joyce Stokes Jones, Eunice Greene, and Michele Jones Galvin (far right). Alice Norris was married to Harry Norris who grew up in the former residence of Harriet Tubman Davis.

Alice Norris' recollections and documentation were fundamental to reconstructing the last chapter of this book. (circa 2009)

AFTERWORD

—

We all have a story, even you. We have a past, a present, and a future that are shaped by our beginnings. Our families, communities, faith, values, or lack thereof shape the story. You have now read my story and that of Harriet Tubman within the context of her family.

The story of President Barack Obama's historic presidential candidacy led 53 million Americans and myself to catapult him into the most esteemed position in the world. As I was concluding my research and writings on my great-great-grandaunt Harriet Tubman, something happened that I never would have thought to happen in my lifetime. An African American would be president of the United States of America. After conducting more than thirty years' worth of research and writing, it never dawned on me that my life would be impacted by the election of the first black president. Like the forty-three presidents before him, Obama would be the leader of the free world. Only in America could the son of an African man from Kenya and a white woman from Kansas rise from the schools of Indonesia to the halls of Harvard to the political landscape of the United States Senate to the presidency of the United States.

At this writing, I am eighty-one. Like millions of other Americans, I cast my vote on November 4, 2008, for the then Senator Barack Obama. As I approached the election-voting site at Transfiguration Church at Teall Avenue in Syracuse, New York, I was transfixed on the long walkway leading to the basement of the church. I simply could not believe that I was ready, willing, and able to march myself up to the voting booth, where I would be casting my vote in a historic election—for a black man. A black man had earned the nomination of the Democratic Party for president of the United States. Wild horses could not have kept me from voting that day. Along with my family and friends and almost everyone I knew, pride and purpose filled our hearts and minds. Not knowing what the outcome would be, we all knew that the election would be a defining moment in our nation's history. That election, more than any other that I had voted in, clearly resonated that every vote counts.

It was a beautiful fall day here in Central New York. After Halloween, one never knows what kind of weather will embrace us, but this day was special. The sun shown brightly and the skies were robin's-egg blue. By every account, the weather was seasonably comfortable. Snow, wind, and rain had no place here. My daughter Michele accompanied me as I walked through the entrance to the polling place. Proudly, I walked in and signed the registered voters' log. The polling attendants seemed to be particularly friendly and talkative. One of the women, for my district, commented that the number of votes already cast seemed to surpass the numbers cast by that time of day in years past.

Seemingly energized, she walked me to the voting booth and waited outside while I pulled the curtain securely closed behind me. There it was. The line up of democrat politicians running for election was as plain as day. Leading the pack was Obama/Biden. Without hesitation, I slowly but surely pulled down the small metal lever next to Obama/Biden. It was exhilarating. It was liberating. I had voted for the first African American to be nominated for president of the United States. With that done, I was deliberate about clicking my way through the democrat line. I was careful not to click the name of one democrat politician who I did not want to vote for. I still pride myself on voting for the person. Voting "no" for her did not diminish my thorough satisfaction with voting for the others.

(Obama, y'all!)

As we left the voting place, I was acutely aware of the moment. I could not help but to express my understanding that it was an extraordinary time. I could not believe that I was finally voting for someone of my race for president. It would not have been difficult to become overwhelmed with emotion. Instead, I smiled to myself and my thoughts drifted to my husband, my daughter, my parents, my grandparents, and all of those who had since passed away. I could not help but to think that they were all with me in spirit that day. I reckoned with the simple truth that this had not happened in their day, but it had happened in my lifetime. It was awesome. I had lived long enough to see my vote cemented with the majority of America to elect Barack Obama.

Whether one agrees with his politics or not, it cannot be lost on any of us that, as Americans, we have come a long way from slavery to equal opportunity. When I say we, I mean blacks and whites, Native Americans, Hispanics, Asians, and others. I mean the poor, the middle class, and those with more than enough. I mean the religious and the non-religious. I mean those who are able and the disabled. I mean those who identify as heterosexual, homosexual, bisexual, and transgender. America has spoken. America and the world will never be the same.

(Hallelujah!)

We can thank Martin Luther King, Jr. for opening our minds and hearts to judging a man or woman by the content of their character and not by the color of their skin.

(Hallelujah!)

I think of Modesty, my great-great-great-grandmother. She was uprooted and taken from her family and everything she knew in Ghana, West Africa. We believe she was of the Ashanti people. She endured the torture and humiliation of the slave route of Assin Praso to Assin Manso to the slave dungeons of Elmina Castle to the auction block of the Eastern Shore of Maryland. Let's be reminded that only the strong survived. I think of her daughter Rittia, born to her and a white man. Their blood runs through each and every one of us, including her granddaughter Harriet. Harriet was known as Araminta as a young girl. She escaped from slavery as a young married woman. As a freedom seeker, her life's work was to rescue black men, women, and children and resettle them in the northern states of America and Canada. She was a simple, humble, yet determined woman who would rather live free than die as a slave. She was committed to ensuring that other blacks achieved the same goal.

Aunt Harriet, undoubtedly, wanted the same for her immediate family. Although she married twice in her life, she made it quite clear that she had no biological children. Many historians have held to the romantic notion that she had "adopted" children. Their insistence does not create a familial blood tie where one does not exist. Aunt Harriet loved her people. Whenever she could, she took in children, adults, and the elderly. She made a home for them when they had none of their own. Getting to know her through research and family stories, I am certain that if she had biological children of her own we would all know of them. Those of us who know of our lineage connecting us to the great American heroine know that we are related by blood through one of her sisters or brothers.

History and documentation has gone a long way in helping family members to establish that connection. By blood and/or marriage, we are excited to be connected to the woman and the legacy of a fearless and ferocious freedom seeker.

In my immediate family, I think of my grandmother Mary Elliott Gaskin. She was the daughter of Ann Marie Ross Stewart and Thomas Elliott. Ann Marie was the daughter of Sophe—Harriet Tubman's sister. Sophe was married at the time, but was sold into slavery when her only child, Ann Marie, was about three-months-old. As a suckling babe, we believe that Ann Marie was reared by her grandparents Rittia and Ben. Ann Marie also enjoyed the love and protection of her aunt Harriet and her Uncles Ben, Robert, Harry, Moses, and Henry. With sisters Sophe and Linah sold into slavery, we believe that little Ann Marie (a niece) was raised as a sister. Blood ties were extremely important. Like other slave families, the Rosses took care of their own. History teaches us some very important lessons. We can't take back what has already occurred, but we can change the future.

Ann Marie and Thomas Elliott were the parents of my grandmother Marietta (Mary) Elliott who married Phillip Gaskin. My mother, Alida, was the youngest of their eleven children. From Modesty to Rit to Harriet to Sophe to Ann Marie to Marietta to Alida to me, there were six generations grounded in family values that have stood the test of time. I hope that my husband, Harry, and I have passed on those values to our children, and they to their children. My greatest hope is that these values will pervade for future generations. I saw these values abided by in my young life on a daily basis. From my parents care of my mother's aunt Martha, who was suffered from senility, to their care of Mr. Allen, who suffered from epileptic seizures, to opening our home to black prisoners, who were released from Auburn State Prison. It was always clear to me that it was our obligation to give honor to God, take care of the family, and assist neighbors whenever possible. Simply said, but it often took courage and compassion to actually do it.

I think of all of them now. I wonder what they would think about life in America now that we have a black president. I know for certain that the election of Barack Obama would have amazed them, as it did me. His ascension to the presidency meant that a majority of Americans—white and black—heard his message. A majority of Americans looked past his race and looked toward what he could or would legislate for the good of most Americans. Even more than that, he gives something to our country that was not captured in the values that my family held dear. He gives hope to the children of color in our nation. For the first time, they all can truly believe that they can be the best they can be. They can imagine themselves being who they want to be. All children can dream the dream. Red, brown, yellow, black, or white, children all over the world can finally say to themselves that hope is alive. They can say that, "I can be who I want to be." No longer will they simply mouth the words, but they know that it can actually come true.

That is what Barack Obama means for all of our children. He gives hope and a vision of what can be. Just as importantly, the parents, extended family, and teachers of our children can instill in them not only the values of faith and love, but also the esteemed value of hope. With hope, the children who are our future can transform the world. I believe that all of my faithful and loving ancestors would wave their hands over their heads and say amen to that.

Four years later, it happened again. With a hard-won campaign, the people of the United States of America reelected Barack Obama. It is an awesome feeling of relief to know that we have a man in the people's house that leads with understanding and compassion. So many problems face our nation. We can only hope that the people will stand with President Barack Obama to reclaim a prosperous America. So much remains to be done. In the words of Aunt Harriet, let's "keep on moving!"

BIBLIOGRAPHY

—

Adams, Samuel Hopkins. "A Slave in the Family" (from *Grandfather Stories*). New York: Random House, 1947.

Albert, B. "Africans Put Out the Welcome Mat for African Americans." *The Post Standard.* April 4, 1998, A-4.

Bains, Rae. *Harriet Tubman: The Road to Freedom.* Troll Communications L.L.C., 1982.

Bentley, Judith. *Harriet Tubman.* Franklin Watts, 1990.

Blassingame, John. *Slave Testimony: Two Centuries of Letters, Speeches, Interviews, and Autobiographies.* Louisiana State University Press, 1977.

Bledsoe, Lucy Jane. *Harriet Tubman.* Quercus Corp, 1987.

Bradford, Sarah H. *Harriet Tubman: The Moses of Her People.* New York: Corinth Books Inc., 1961.

Brown, Ira V. *The Negro in Pennsylvania History.* University Park, PA: Pennsylvania Historical Association, 1970.

Campbell, Edward D.C. and Kym S. Rice. *Before Freedom Came: African-American Life in the Antebellum South.* Museum of Confederacy, Charlottesville: Richmond and University of Virginia, 1991.

Carlson, Judy. *Harriet Tubman: Call to Freedom Great Lives Series.* Ballantine Books, Random House Publishing Group, 1989.

Carter, Polly. *Harriet Tubman and Black History Month.* Silver Burdett Pr, 1996.

Clifford Larson, Kate. *Bound for the Promised Land: Harriet Tubman, Portrait of an American Hero.* New York: Ballantine Books, 2004.

Clinton, Catherine. *Harriet Tubman: The Road to Freedom.* Waltham, MA: Little, Brown & Company, 2005.

Conrad, Earl. *Harriet Tubman.* Washington, D.C.: The Associated Publishers, 1943.

Cottrol, Robert. *From African to Yankee: Narratives of Slavery and Freedom in Antebellum New England.* Armonk, NY: M.E. Sharpe Inc., 1998.

Darby, Penney and Peter Stastny. *The Lives They Left Behind.* Bellevue Literary Press, 2008.

"Dreams Realized." Syracuse, NY: *The Sunday Herald,* April 19, 1896.

Du Bois, W.E.B. *The Philadelphia Negro: A Social Study.* Philadelphia: University of Pennsylvania Press, 1995.

Ferris, Jeri. *Go Free or Die: A Story about Harriet Tubman.* Lerner Publishing Group, 1988.

Fields, Barbara Jeanne. *Slavery and Freedom on the Middle Ground: Maryland During the Nineteenth Century.* New Haven, CT: Yale University Press, 1984.

Franklin, John Hope and Alfred Moss, Jr. *From Slavery to Freedom: A History of Negro Americans* (Sixth Edition). New York: Knopf, 1988.

Green, William. *Narrative of Events in the Life of William Green, (Formerly a Slave).* Springfield, MA: L. M. Guernsey, 1853.

Haley, Alex. *Roots: The Saga of an American Family.* Garden City, NY: Doubleday and Company, Inc. 1976.

Haskins, Jim. *Get on Board: The Story of the Underground Railroad.* New York: Scholastic Press, 1993.

Humez, Jean M. *Harriet Tubman: The Life and the Life Stories.* Madison, WI: University of Wisconsin Press, 2003

Hunter, Carol. *To Set the Captives Free: Reverand Jermain Wesley Loguen and the struggle for freedom in Central New York.* New York: Garland Press, 1993.

Klees, Emerson. *Underground Railroad Tales: With Routes Through the Finger Lakes Region.* Rochester, NY: Friends of the Finger Lakes, 1997.

McClard, Megan. *Harriet Tubman: Slavery and the Underground Railroad* (History of the Civil War Series). Englewood Cliffs, NJ: Silver Burdett Pr, 1991.

McGowan, James A. *Station Master on the Underground Railroad: The Life and Letters of Thomas Garrett.* Moylan, PA: Whimsie Press, 1977.

McPherson, James M. *This Mighty Scourge: Perspectives on the Civil War.* New York: Oxford University Press, 2007.

Meier, August and Elliott Rudwick. *From Plantation to Ghetto* (American Century). New York: Hill and Wang, 1970.

Mowbray, Calvin W. and Maurice D. Rimpo. *Close-ups of Early Dorchester County History* (Second Edition). Silver Spring, MD: Family Line Publications, 1988.

Pattison, Atthow. "The last will and testament of Atthow Pattison." Dorchester County, 1791.

Quarles, Benjamin. *Black Abolitionists.* New York: Oxford University Press, 1969.

Ross, B. Chattel. Record FJH No. 2, folio 163, Dorchester County: 1855.

Siebert, Wilbur H. *The Underground Railroad* (1898 original). New York: Arno Press and *The New York Times,* 1968.

Sterling, Dorothy. *We Are Your Sisters: Black Women in the Nineteenth Century.* New York: W.W. Norton & Company, 1984.

Still, William. *The Underground Railroad.* Philadelphia: 1872.

Thomas, Velma Maia. *Lest We Forget: the Passage from Africa to Slavery and Emancipation.* New York: Crown Publishers, 1997.

Wellman, Judith. "Uncovering the Freedom Trail in Auburn and Cayuga County" (Historical Report). New York: 2004-05.

ABOUT *the* AUTHORS

—

Joyce Stokes Jones was born on December 31, 1929, in Auburn, New York—the home and death place of Harriet Ross Tubman. Jones attended Seward Elementary School and later graduated from West High School in 1948. She met Harry Jones, Jr. in Buffalo, New York, and the two were married on June 16, 1951. Jones graduated from Bryant & Stratton College in June 1952. Jones was a career secretary, and she retired in 1989 after fifteen years as secretary to the president of the Syracuse Common Council. Beginning in the early 1970s, Jones began her thirty years of research and writing about the life and times of her great-great-grandaunt Harriet Ross Tubman.

In 1968, Jones contracted with *The Syracuse Herald Journal* to write a weekly column called "Black Heritage," which depicted notable African American figures in American history. During that same year, she produced a children's segment on black heritage at Channel 9 WSYR. Later in 1970, Jones was commissioned by New Readers Press to write a column entitled "Blacks in Time." Two years later, she was hired at WCNY/Channel 24 to produce and direct thirty-minute segments on issues within the local black community.

Jones has given numerous presentations to students and congregations and community forums on Harriet Tubman's life. She has also conducted tours at the Tubman Home. Her travels have taken her to such places as Annapolis, Cambridge, and Bucktown, Maryland. She has also visited St. Catharines, Canada, Cleveland, Ohio, New York City, Washington, D.C., Philadelphia, Pennsylvania, and Auburn, New York. Jones made these trips in search of relevant information, and she was often led to new and different discoveries about her famous relative.

In 1985, Jones produced a documentary video on Harriet Tubman's life based on her findings that was called *A Conversation with a Living Relative of Harriet Tubman.* Later in February 1992, she designed and handcrafted the limited edition Harriet Tubman doll. The doll was modeled after the author's late daughter, Olivia Babette Jones, who resembled the famous Conductor of the Underground Railroad.

In October 1999, Jones was motivated to compile her research and writings to author *Beyond the Underground: Aunt Harriet, Moses of Her People.* It chronicles her investigation into circumstances and significant events that shaped the lives of the Green Ross family, while focusing on Harriet Ross Tubman, one of America's greatest and bravest heroines. It is a poignant story that details the nuances and realities of slavery on the Eastern Shore of Maryland, and alludes to the paradox of winning freedom in the northern states and Canada. The backbone of this work explores the relationships between family members, their masters, and friends, all of whom helped to create the Harriet Tubman saga. The manuscript is more dynamic and humbling than is often documented.

Jones was recognized by the Syracuse Common Council for her work to preserve and perpetuate the legacy of Harriet Tubman. She served on the board of directors of the Onondaga Historical Society. She was a member of the Urban League Harriet Tubman Award Committee. She was also awarded the Bethany Baptist Church Spirit of Harriet Tubman Award. The local chapter of the National Organization of Women recognized Jones with its Unsung Heroine Award. She was also inducted into the North Side Hall of Fame.

Jones is retired and resides in Syracuse, New York.

Michele Jones Galvin is the Director of Community Initiatives in the Department of Social Services and the former director of the ACCESS Center. The ACCESS Center was an infant mortality prevention program sponsored by the Department of Social Services. ACCESS, a centralized case management information system, was designed to ensure the coordination of contract agencies providing case management services, streamline the referral process, monitor case activity, and track services for families who are at risk for infant death.

Currently, Jones Galvin is responsible to assist the commissioner of social services with data management, coordination, and evaluation of community-based special projects. She works closely with administrators of community-based organizations, schools, and health and social service programs to provide families the greatest access to medical care and support services that will significantly improve health outcomes and promote self-sufficiency. Jones Galvin specializes in program design, implementation, and evaluation. Her areas of expertise also include communication, collaboration, coordination, strategic planning, outreach, supervision, and board relations. In support of the county's commitment to valuing diversity in the workplace, Jones Galvin is a member of the diversity training leadership team and a certified Bridges Out of Poverty facilitator.

Before relocating to Syracuse, Jones Galvin worked as a systems training and testing coordinator for Human Resources Administration in New York City. In 1985, she was awarded a masters degree in psychological research from the New School for Social Research. In 1980, she received a bachelors degree with a double major in psychology and African American studies from Fordham University.

Jones Galvin serves on the board of directors of the George and Rebecca Barnes Foundation, HealtheConnections RHIO of Central New York, and Loretto Nursing Home. She formerly served as a board member for Centers for Nature Education, Chadwick Residence, Consolidated Industries, Cultural Resources Council, Everson Museum, HOME, Inc., Juneteenth, Inc., Independent Living Services, Junior League of Syracuse, Loretto Corporate, Meals on Wheels, North East Community Center, Partners in Education and Business, PEACE, Inc., Regional Learning Services, Syracuse Corinthian Club, Syracuse Stage Guild, Transitional Living Services, Vera House, Volunteer Center, and Women's Fund of Central New York.

Jones Galvin is also affiliated with Community Wide Dialogue on Race, FOCUS Greater Syracuse, Junior League of Syracuse, Lambda Kappa Mu, Inc., Leadership Greater

Syracuse, National Coalition Building Institute, Professionals of Color, Syracuse Citizen's Academy, and Thursday Morning Roundtable. She was the recipient of the Onondaga County Martin Luther King Award in 1998 and the Lambda Kappa Mu Service Award in 2001. In 2002, Jones Galvin was awarded the Thursday Morning Roundtable Award for Meritorious Community Service and the YWCA Diversity Achiever's Award. In 2007, she was inducted into the North Side Hall of Fame. In 2008, Jones Galvin was recognized as one of the founders of the Women's Fund of Central New York, and in 2009, she was awarded the Bethany Baptist Church Harriet Tubman Spirit Award. She was awarded the American Red Cross Women Who Mean Business Award in 2011.

Jones Galvin and her mother, Joyce Stokes Jones, began collaborating on a creative nonfiction book in 1999. The work is based on genealogical research and their family ties to Harriet Ross Tubman, Conductor of the Underground Railroad. It chronicles the family saga from the survival of the Middle Passage to slavery on the Eastern Shore of Maryland to freedom in Canada, and then settling in Central New York. Told from the perspective of a relative, *Beyond the Underground: Aunt Harriet, Moses of Her People* portrays the life, times, and accomplishments of the famed abolitionist. The book culminates as it speaks to the pivotal role of race, color, and discrimination as counterpoints in the lives of Tubman and her great-great-grandniece Joyce Stokes Jones. Jones Galvin resides in Syracuse, New York, with her husband, John. Their son, John Jr., resides in Washington, D.C.

CONNECT *with the* AUTHORS

E-MAIL
mjgalvin@mosesofherpeople.com
sankofamediaone@gmail.com

FACEBOOK
Beyond the Underground: Aunt Harriet,
Moses of Her People

TWITTER
@MosesofHerPpl

WEBSITE
www.mosesofherpeople.com